Leicestershire Legends

retold by

Black Annis

Heart of Albion Press

Leicestershire Legends retold by Black Annis

Cover illustration by Jenny Clarke

ISBN 1 872883 77 X

Published by
Heart of Albion Press
2 Cross Hill Close, Wymeswold
Loughborough, LE12 6UJ

albion@indigogroup.co.uk

Visit our Web site: www.hoap.co.uk

Printed in the UK by Booksprint

Contents

Preface

The importance of dialect

Despite the tendency in recent decades for traditional tales to be written in bland, 'standardised' English, it takes little imagination to realise that these tales survived – often for centuries – as stories that were *spoken* rather than written down. Even when tales have been recorded – for example in the rather florid poems of the late eighteenth century – the tales have still been told in more informal styles. Indeed the very nature of telling traditional tales implies an informal occasion – over a pint or three in a pub, or an afternoon cup of tea. We are all aware, even if we rarely consciously think about it, that written English is more 'formal' than the way we speak. However with traditional tales which are closely linked to specific places there is another aspect that is usually ignored – the local people who knew these tales and kept them alive would also have quite distinctive local accents, pronunciation and dialect words.

For the purposes of this preface the word 'dialect' will be used as an abbreviation for all aspects of dialect, accent and pronunciation even though, for the specialist, the word dialect refers to *words* and phrases spoken locally (and rarely, if ever, used in writing) rather than to the accent and pronunciation.

In marked contrast to most other parts of Britain, the dialects of the East Midlands have received almost no study. This is especially true for Leicestershire as, apart from some the sketchy detail provided in national surveys, the only other recent publications have been restricted to the dialect of Leicester itself, which ignores the wide diversity elsewhere in the county – which include the very distinctive pronunciation of the Shepshed and Coalville area to the north-west of Charnwood Forest, and the start of the transition to the quite different West Midlands 'sing song' in the Hinckley area. In the east part of the county – imagine a triangular area centred on the A47 road, with the point close to the eastern suburbs of Leicester and the wide part encompassing Rutland – the influence of Lincolnshire and

Northamptonshire dialects give a more subtle shift to the dialect, with the traditional Rutland dialects quite distinct from Leicester city ones.

A 'softened' version of the Leicester city dialect can be found upstream and downstream along the Soar valley, and into the Wreake valley towards Melton Mowbray. Indeed this accent is related to other accents of the Trent valley and its tributaries, such as the Erewash valley between Derbyshire and Nottinghamshire. For example the greeting 'Eh up m'duck!', considered to by many to be unique to Leicester, is used as far as way as Ilkeston. The links between dialects and topography (and , in turn, traditional travel routes such as rivers) mean that the dialect in the Vale of Belvoir is similar on both the Leicestershire and Nottinghamshire sides, as are the accents on both banks of the River Welland which forms the Leicestershire-Northamptonshire boundary (although these Northamptonshire influences drop off sharply outside the fairly narrow Welland valley and do not extend very far into Leicestershire).

Since the 1950s the British population generally has become more mobile, and one aspect of this has been the 'repopulation' of rural villages by people who were not born or brought up in the locality. The higher prices of houses in most rural parts of the East Midlands also means that people born in these villages are often unable to buy their own homes there, so move into nearby towns. Indeed, the increasing tendency of people to go off to university in other parts of the country soon after they are eighteen means that ties to 'home' are fractured early in life. Nevertheless, there are still people in all parts of Leicestershire who have spent all their lives living in the same village or suburb and who speak in ways that are subtly distinct from those who have lived all their lives just a few villages away.

'Newcomers' predominate in most Leicestershire and Rutland villages. These are increasingly people who were previously living in the south-east of England where so-called 'Estuary English' has become the socially-accepted accent and displaced many traditional accents. Estuary English is a term invented in the 1980s to refer to a diluted form of Cockney adopted by the younger middle classes – think of the accent of Michael Caine, Janet Street Porter, Jonathan Ross or Ben Elton. While Estuary English has become widespread as close as Northamptonshire and Cambridgeshire it has not, so far, taken over Leicestershire in the same way. This is presumably because Estuary English uses the long 'a' sound (e.g. in 'bath' [barth] and 'grass' [*grarss*]) whereas Leicestershire (and counties to the north) use the short 'a' sound, so such words are pronounced 'as written'. However Estuary English is already commonly heard in Rutland, because of the high proportion of 'immigrants' from the Home Counties living there. As the traditional Rutland accent is closer to Northamptonshire rather than Leicestershire, it will be interesting to see if people native to Rutland adopt Estuary English more readily than in Leicestershire.

While the coming together of large numbers of people in factories in the second half of the nineteenth century helped to conserve or even enhance dialect, the advent of national primary education around 1870 was a formidable anti-dialect force. School teachers imposed Standard English. Indeed teachers' middle class distaste for dialect has been maintained until the present day, and positive opposition to dialect was incorporated into the National Curriculum in 1993. Dialect speech has few champions as it is associated with the rural and urban working classes. As such it falls outside the scope of middle class nostalgia for an imaginary idyllic England that has pervaded interest in the past in recent decades.

As will readily become apparent, Black Annis is most certainly not middle class and, while she does not discuss her education, some rather sharp-tongued remarks suggest that her encounters with teachers have not left very favourable impressions! When Black Annis was retelling these local legends it was very tempting to retain her distinctive Leicester way of speaking. However books written entirely in dialect are very tiresome to read so, a little reluctantly, these tales have been edited for publication to conform with standard English spelling. ('Standard English' is the term used to refer to a form of English that is spoken by no one; the term reflects the recommended usage of English which is typical of educated *written* forms of English.) However other aspects of Black Annis's way of talking have been retained, such as local forms of grammar – for example, the verbs ' was' and 'were' are often used in ways that standard English would regard as wrong. However, when Black Annis recounts her conversations with various friends (who all have much more pronounced dialect and accents) their way of speaking has been represented as accurately as is possible, even though this means that both grammar and spelling are often quite distinct from standard English. Nevertheless, anyone serious about the study of dialect will dismiss such a mixture of regional terms with non-standard English as merely 'literary dialect'.

To help those reading this book who are less familiar with Leicestershire dialect then the guide to Leicester dialect on the following pages may be helpful.

If you live in Leicestershire and are interested in studying the dialect of your locality and would like to be put in contact with other researchers then please write to:

Leicestershire Dialect Study Group
c/o Heart of Albion Press
2 Cross Hill Close, Wymeswold
Loughborough, LE12 6UJ

Bob Trubshaw

Wymeswold, June 2004

Guide to Leicester dialect

Based on Clifford Dunkley's *Let's Talk Leicester* by kind permission of Clifford Dunkley.

East Midlands vowel pronunciation is a comparatively plain and unadorned compared to the ornate vowel distortions of some accents (e.g. West Country 'moy' for 'my' or Geordy 'pleeut' for 'plate'), the singsong intonation of West Midlands dialects, or the nasal tendencies of Scouse.

The main characteristic of Leicester pronunciation is the avoidance of exertion to re-configure the mouth. **So length** and **strength** become 'lenth' and 'strenth', **with** becomes 'wi', **and** becomes 'n'. 'F' and 'v' sounds sometimes change to 'n', so **never heard of it** becomes 'never 'erd on it'. More extreme contractions include **do you**, which becomes 'jer', **anything** which shrinks to 'ote', and **nothing** which reduces to 'nowt'

Although Leicester dialect includes some frequently-used double negatives such as 'I don't know nowt about it' and 'can't do nowt about it', grammar follows pronunciation in usually taking the line of least resistance. So the past tense of the verb 'to be' becomes 'I were', 'he were', 'she were' and 'they were' (although, exceptionally, 'was' is used – when Standard English would use 'were'! – in 'was yer wantin ote?'). Similarly 'come' is substituted for **came**, 'gen' for **gave**, 'done' for **did** and 'knowed' for **knew**. 'Us' is substituted for **our**, and can also be substituted for 'me', as in 'giz us a fag'. **My** often changes to me' as in 'where's me shoes?'. 'Wot' (**what**) replaces the relative pronouns **which, who** and **whom** e.g. 'That comic wot ah read', 'That man wot passed me', 'That gal wot ah saw'. Sometimes 'us' (pronounced more like 'uz') replaces **who** in 'im uz limps' (**he who limps**) or 'er uz speaks posh' (**she who speaks properly**). **Who are** changes to 'them as is'.

Plural subjects are also used with singular verbs in expressions such as 'There in't many keks left.' (**there aren't many cakes left**) and similarly 'them' often replaces **those** e.g. in 'them's good uns' (**they are good ones**).

The simple past form is usually substituted for the past participle, so 'ay's ett the last cob' (**I have eaten the last bread roll**), 'who's drank it all?' (**who has drunk it all?**), 'we done it!' (**we did it**), 'ah seen 'em yestadah' (**I saw them yesterday**), 'ey's wrote a letta' (**he has written a**

viii

letter), 'the cat's fell in th' worta' (**the cat has fallen in the water**), 'er's trod in sum mud' (**she has trodden in some mud**) and 'it stunk' (**it stank**).

In many dialects strong verbs (i.e. those that change their internal vowel to form the past tense e.g. swim/swam, teach/taught, tell/told) often change to weak verbs (where '-ed', '-d' or '-t' are added to form the past tense). Leicester is no exception so 'ay noed im' (**I knew him**), 'ay've noed im fer ten year' (**I have known him for ten years**), 'ay telled im' (**I told him**), 'it growed' (**it grew**), 'ay catched im when ee popped rahnd this mornin' (**I caught him when he popped around this morning**). However watch out for 'it owny sempt like yestadah' (**it only seemed like yesterday**) and 'yuh gin me te much' (**you have given me too much**), 'ay'd abaht gin yuh up' (**I had about given up on you**) and 'eh gev im a good idin' (**he gave him a good hiding**).

'Off' is used only as an adverb (as a preposition **off** changes to 'off of', as in 'ay bawt it off of im up road') so 'e ad is money took off of im'. 'Off' also appears as an intensive particle when 'start' is used as a noun in 'for a start off'.

To add emphasis the object pronoun ('him', 'her') is used e.g. 'er with gloves on' (**that woman with the gloves on**) or 'im with Rolls' (**that man with the Rolls Royce**).

When asking questions the opening 'Are' is often omitted, so 'you in an urry?' (**Are you in a hurry?**) or 'you not commin?' (**Are you not coming?**). The distinction between 'shall' and 'will' has long been blurred in Standard English because of the contraction '-'ll'. However older speakers of Leicester dialect sometimes added emphasis to interrogative commands by using forms such as 'Shall yuh come?' or 'Shall yuh close the door, please?' (although Standard English is **Will you come?** and **Will you close the door, please?**); this usage now seems to have died out.

The full 'u'

The 'u' in bus, custom, sun, etc is pronounced 'uh' so **love** ('luhv'), **son** ('suhn')

Exceptions are **mother** ('motha'), **bugger** ('bugga'), **come** ('com') [N.B. **came** and **comb** are also pronounced 'com'.]

The short 'a'

The 'a' in **after, plaster, grass, ask, laughter, bath, glass, brass, alabaster, broadcast, aircraft is** pronounced 'as written', and *not* arfter, plarstah, arsk, larfter, barth, glarss, brarss, alabarstah, broadcarst, aircrarft. (The final 'er' of **after, laughter, albaster, broadcaster** is however pronounced almost the same, becoming afta, lafta, alabasta, broadcasta.)

Exceptions are **half** ('ahf), **father** (fahtha) and **water** (worta)

variants on 'a'

'al' usually sounds more like 'poll' e.g. **alter** (olta), **fault** (folt), **false** (folse)

want becomes wont. **swan** becomes swon.

shake becomes shek, **make** becomes mek, **take** becomes tek, **great** becomes gret

have becomes 'av, but **have you** becomes 'ay ya

The 'ar' sound is sometimes lengthened, so **card** becomes 'caard', **park** 'paark',

'ew'

new is pronounced 'noo'. Likewise **tune** becomes 'toon'.

short 'oo'

bloody becomes 'bleddeh'

lengthened 'oo'

don't becomes 'doon't', **go** sometimes (e.g. at end of sentences) becomes 'goo' (although more usually becomes 'guh'), **won't** becomes 'woon't'

'i'

girl becomes 'gel'

aspirate 'h'

The aspirate 'h' is usually omitted. Where this follows 'the' the final 'e' of **the** is lengthened, so **the house** becomes 'thee ouse'.

medial 'g'

The effort needed to enunciate the medial 'g' of **length** and **strength** is incompatible with Leicester speech, so become 'lenth' and 'strenth'.

medial 'd'

Likewise the 'd' of **could not**, **did not**, **should not** and **would not** is dropped, becoming 'coon't', 'din't', 'shun't' and 'woon't'.

The medial 'th' in **clothes** is omitted to become 'cloes'. **The medial 'l'** in **only** is dropped to become 'ony'. Medial syllables omitted include **generally** ('genly'), **properly** ('proply'), **direction** ('drection'), **collection** ('clection') and **regular** ('reggler').

final '-ow'

window becomes 'winda'; thus: 'is fahtha's a winda cleana'. **arrow** becomes 'arra'. **follow** becomes 'folla'

final '-y'

'y' at the end of words usually becomes 'eh', so **mucky** becomes 'muckeh'.

final 'ing'

The 'g' of '-ing' is almost always omitted. So **talking** becomes 'talkin'.

final 'ter' and 'ther'

Words such as **water, daughter** are pronounced with the emphasis on the first syllable and the 'ter' pronounced with the minimum of effort, so tend towards 'wor'ra' and 'dor'ra'. As with most English dialects, **brother** and **mother** sound like 'brutha' and 'motha'.

final 'th'

'-th' at the end of words is usually dropped. So **with** becomes 'wi'

final 'self'

'yourself' and 'myself' usually contact to 'you' and 'me'. So 'ay yer washed yuh?' (**have you washed yourself?**) or 'ay dressed me' (**I dressed myself**).

Likewise 'afterwards' sometimes contracts to 'after' (we'd berra do that after').

Other variations from Standard English

Another common contraction is to drop adverbs such as 'there' and 'that', as in 'ay can't get' (**I can't get there**). Adverbs are often used differently to Standard English ('e wer that poorly' **he was so poorly** and the responses to 'it's a nice day' such as 'it is that' or 'it is n'all'). Similarly adjectives can be swapped, as in 'a fortnight since' (**a fortnight ago**).

Conjunctions sometimes swap too, such as 'as how' replacing **that** e.g. 'yer no as how he's tight fisted' (**you know that he's miserly**) or added e.g. 'same as ay sed' (**as I said**).

Adding emphasis to the end of sentences

isn't it (pronounced 'in'it') is often added for emphasis at the end of interrogative constructions e.g. 'it in't 'alf 'ot, in'it?' (**it's rather warm, is it not?'**)

Emphasis is often achieved by repetition, as in the previous example, or in constructions such as 'yer've gorra big gob, yer av!' (**you have a large mouth**), or 'e's a right un is Ted' (**he's an exceptional one is Ted**).

'Nah be said' (**that's enough**) is another way of adding emphasis 'ay've towd yer, yer norravin any more sweets, nah *be said*!'

ON A CAVE
called
BLACK ANNIS'S BOWER

being an answer to a very young lady's
enquiries about the story of Black Annis

Where down the plain the winding pathway falls,
From Glenn-field vill, to Lester's ancient walls,
Nature, or Art, with imitative power,
Far in the Glenn has plac'd Black Annis' Bower.

An oak, the pride of all the mossy dell,
Spreads his broad arms above the stony cell;
And many a bush, with hostile thorns array'd,
Forbids the secret cavern to invade;
Whilst delving vales each way meander round,
And violet banks with redolence abound.

Here, if the uncouth song of former days,
Soil not the page with Falsehood's artful lays,
Black Annis held her solitary reign,
The dread and wonder of the neighb'ring plain.

The Shepherd griev'd to view his waning flock,
And trac'd the firstlings to the gloomy rock.
No vagrant children cull'd the flowerets then,
For infant blood oft stain'd the gory den.

Not Sparta Mount* for infant tears renown'd,
Echo'd more frequently the piteous sound.
Oft the gaunt Maid the frantic Mother curs'd,
Whom Britan's wolf with savage nipple nurs'd;
Whilst Lester's sons beheld aghast the scene,
Nor dar'd to meet the Monster of the Green.

'Tis said the soul of mortal man recoil'd
To view Black Annis' eye, so fierce and wild;
Vast talons, foul with human flesh, there grew
In place of hands, and features livid blue
Glar'd in her visage; whilst her obscene waist,
Warm skins of human victims close embrac'd.

But Time, than Man more certain, tho' more slow,
At length 'gainst Annis drew his sable bow;
The great decree the pious Shepherds bless'd,
And general joy the general fear confess'd.

* Mount Taygetus, in a cavern near to which it was the Lacedoemonian custom to expose deformed and weakly children to perish.

From *First Flights* by John Heyrick, junior
Lieutenant in the Fifteenth (or King's) Regiment of Light Dragoons
Published London 1797

Introduction

Introduction

Let's you and I get a thing or two straight. The name's Black Annis, but you may call me 'Cat Anna' between yourselves – but not to my face, if you value the appearance of yours. As any kid growing up in Leicester a while back would tell you, my home used to be Black Annis Bower Close – a posh address for a cave, but that's what happens when you're famous. It were a small outcrop of rock on the Dane Hills; that's off to the west of the city on the way to Glenfield, if you're not from these parts. However after the last World War they weren't interested in the likes of me and a whole load of houses were built there.

When I come into town most folk know I mostly hang around the gateway of the castle, and get some kip in the cellars there. When you've been around as long as me, you'll find out how easy it is to get over from the castle to Dane Hills in the flash of a frog's tongue. The locals tell each other I use an underground tunnel to help me flit about so quickly. Them's that not as sharp as the rest also say I can get to Bradgate and Leicester Abbey using such tunnels. Suits me to let them carry on thinking just that, but no doubt some know better.

Many folk round here still remember my predictions when King Richard III spent his last night in Leicester before the fateful Battle of Bosworth. He and his followers had put up for the night at the Silver Boar Inn – very appropriate as his heraldic emblem was a white or silver boar. By only a little cunningwork I was able to dupe his bodyguards into letting me into his chamber. Whatever he first thought when he saw me enter – after all I was much younger and more attractive then – was soon changed when I raised my hand to give the gesture of greatest warning and bluntly stated 'I have a message for you, Sir' and continued:

The boar that has silver hue
The king's return shall change to blue
The stone that tomorrow his foot shall spurn
Shall strike his head on his return.

The king was understandably troubled and put his face into his hands. I left before he looked up.

The next day as he went past me on his way to Bosworth his spurs struck a stone pillar on Bow Bridge. 'Mark my words.' I said to those around me, 'it'll be his head that'll hit that stone when he comes back.' 'Daft 'a'p-worth' they called me, or worse, though I took scant notice. But I had seen clearly and, after losing the battle, the crown and his life, the king's naked body was thrown across the saddle of a mule and brought back to Leicester. Coming over the bridge, his head was hanging down as low as the stirrups, and it hit that very stone with a whacking great thud.

The new king's soldiers wanted to take Richard's body back to the same inn where he had slept just a few nights before. But they were told there was no Silver Boar Inn. Instead they were taken to where a freshly-painted sign showed a blue boar, as the landlord didn't want the new king to think that he still supported the old king.

Anyways, that's all some time back. Since then I've been getting on in years, and there've been days when the aches and pains make me a bit awkward at times, I'll admit as much myself. I've been known to get a bit upset when silly little kids used to play around outside my cave and shout rude remarks like me being an old witch. When I've showed them I can still move a bit quicker than them and gone on to give them a good hiding, they go off blurting. Usually it's enough for me to warn them off by shouting that I'll belt them so hard as to make them as they want to know their own name. There have been just a few occasions – not more than one or two, I'll swear – when I've got nasty with the little brats and let them have it like nothing again. But they've only got what they asked for, if you want my opinion. There's no reason for their mams to get nasty over it and go around inventing tales about me scratching them to death, eating them and saying it's their hides hanging on my tree.

And as for that eighteenth century gentleman, John Heyrick, he's caused me a world of trouble with his efforts at poetry. My word, I made sure he came to an unsavoury end! Well, what would you do if someone starting to say things like this about you:

> 'Tis said the soul of mortal man recoil'd
> To view Black Annis' eye, so fierce and wild;
> Vast talons, foul with human flesh, there grew
> In place of hands, and features livid blue
> Glar'd in her visage; whilst her obscene waist,
> Warm skins of human victims close embrac'd.

I ain't no rights to be spoken about like that! Anyways, with all these folks calling me so, I've got a bit of a reputation to live down, that's for sure. Every little kid in Leicester used to get told that if they were bad then 'Black Annis'll come and get yer!', and the mothers tittle-tattled about a unpopular neighbour being a 'Cat Anna'.

Let them take my name in vain, see if I care – helps sometimes to be thought a bit tetchy and all. Makes people think you're best not to be messed with. Not that I've ever done more than have words with folk. Well, not that I'd ever own up to, mind. Best leave it that you should do as I say and not as I do – as the parson said when he were liquor struck and they wheeled him home in a wheelbarrow.

And speaking of parsons and their like, all that rumouring about me didn't stop a goodish few of them coming up here to Dane Hills every Easter Monday to see the Mayor and the dignitaries set off for a hare hunt at noon. Well, you know what that type are, they couldn't catch a hare even if a whole coven of witches shape-shifted into furry form in front of them, so they used to get a dead cat, soak it in aniseed, tie it to the tail of a horse and set off at full cry after that. Well, I ask you! Though, so long as it wasn't one of my cats they took and everyone had a good time, I suppose it was all for the best. Anyhow, the fair and the good times got to be more important and it must be four hundred years since anyone did anything like that – even the fair died out by the mid-eighteenth century, if my memory serves me right.

Yes, I know you're wise enough to be thinking I'm even older than I appear to be, ugly old crone that I am. Over in Ireland, when they still respected us Old Ones, they worshipped Anu, so they surmised that a simple slip of the pen is all it would take for me to have once been called Danu, with a temple to me on the tantalisingly similar-sounding Dane Hills. At least that's what a whole bunch of antiquarians kidded themselves into thinking. As for the idea that Danu comes from some foreign floozie calling herself Diana – well, what do you expect from learned professors who spend all their time reading Classics instead of using some common-sense?

Talking to some of the better informed folk around these days, it seems the name Dane Hills doesn't seem to go back any further than 1689, so you can forget about an enclave of Scandinavian bacon makers too. Either some imaginative antiquarian of that time made it up, or it's just a messed up version of the name of the chap, Dannett, who owned these parts in the sixteenth century.

Other fanciful folk have come down to these parts and talked about me as if I were called Brigit, Brigid, Bride or Brigantia, but I don't know much about the likes of them – those names are a bit fancy for round here. Some of them seem to have got into their heads that those Black Virgins that go back to the Middle Ages tie in with Brigid. Because it was a speciality of those dark Madonnas to grant eternal bliss to dead babies, and with my name being Black too, and all that slander about dead kiddies, they've tried to put two and two together. Can't make ends nor sides of all that myself, seems as though they've made two and two into twenty-two.

And they aren't the only folk with a fine sense of nonsense. Some of them that call themselves archaeologists are also a bit overflowing with imagination. This is what one of them came up with. He heard about a memorial brass to an Agnes Scott, who died in 1455, which is still in Swithland church out at Charnwood. She was a Dominican nun who is described on this plaque as being buried in a vault in the church. You can go there and see that much for yourselves, if you don't mind doing a spot of translation from the dog Latin. But the archaeologist wasn't very hot on Latin and thought it said that she was a cave dweller and anchorite. According to our fanciful friend, Agnes's supposed subterranean home was 'probably near Dane Hills' and so 'the memory of a solitary nun dressed in black Dominican robes could well have engendered the folk memory of Black Annis'. As if to support this, he says that 'curiously, a modern convent now stands in the same area' (he means the Convent of St Catherine right by the Glenfield Road). This is the sort of silliness that happens when you can't read Latin right. However an historian called Ronald Hutton seems to have done his homework much better. He said this about Agnes and the confusion with myself:

> 'The gentle and pious Agnes seems... to have been turned first into a local saint, then into a local demon, next into a Celtic goddess, and finally into a witch goddess; and all the while her bones have rested in apparent peace at Swithland.'

Need I say more!

Anyways, you don't want me ranting on about myself all the time as there's plenty of other interesting legends from in and around Leicester.

How folk say Leicester started

Chapter 1

How folk say Leicester started

It says in a book – so it must be true, eh – that King Leir built a city on the River Soar which was named after him and called Caerleir. The book was written in the first half of the twelfth century, not long after the Norman conquest. The chap who wrote it down we call Geoffrey of Monmouth. He was the first to write a history of the kings of England. It's a bit light on facts and generous with imaginative bits as it was written to appeal to the new Norman lords and masters – so you can trust it about as much as one of today's political spin doctors. He must have judged quite well what he thought these Normans wanted to hear, as his book was a big success. He went on to write another book about the life of the wizard Merlin, which has become the basis of many centuries of legends.

Well, Geoffrey includes a bit about Leicester and says that King Leir lived 2,000 before him, which certainly don't fit what we now know about prehistory. As for thinking that the city he founded would have been called Caerleir, this is dead wonky as such a name could only have been invented after the Romans came, whereas Leir was dead long before then.

Fact is, we don't know a lot about King Leir except what Geoffrey tells us, so fortunately he spins a good yarn. Shakespeare was quite fond of taking stories from Geoffrey of Monmouth's history of English kings, and his play King Lear develops Geoffrey's remarks about the king's three daughters into a long complicated story about the king in his old age which involves wandering around some desolate heaths and woods in the pouring rain. As Shakespeare almost certainly performed his plays in Leicester, some folk have suggested that he had Charnwood Forest in mind when writing about that storm-drenched wilderness. Who really knows though?

Geoffrey also tells us that King Leir was the grandson of the King Ludd, who also appears in Irish legends as a god. As it happens, King Ludd is remembered elsewhere in Leicestershire, as there are some Anglo-Saxon boundary ditches called King Lud's Entrenchments on Saltby Heath near Sproxton. Odd place to be named after an Irish god though, if you ask me.

The final information that Geoffrey gives us about King Leir is that, after he died, his youngest daughter Cordelia buried his body in a cave under the River Soar – which sounds more than a tad unlikely. By the nineteenth century this story had become a bit grander and the cave had become a temple to Janus. That's storytelling for you – ain't it always the way that everything ends up a bit grander, a bit more whatever, each time it's told.

And if Geoffrey of Monmouth's account of the founding of Leicester seems over fanciful, then it's as nothing compared to another oft-repeated legend. This says that the Irish sea-god Llyr, no less, emerged from the waves to take a human as his wife. He then founded the city of Llyrcester. However the legend doesn't say what an Irish sea-god was doing so far from the sea as Leicester is. In Ireland there were other legends about Llyr and his three sons and at least one storyteller has retold these legends as if they took place in and around Leicester instead of over in Ireland. As if to balance Leir's three daughters, Llyr had three children. The oldest was a son called Bran. He had a sister called Branwen. The third kid was called Efnisien and, as might be expected, he didn't exactly thank folk for having such a daft name. Indeed, he was a mardy brat through and through, and was thoroughly spiteful to his brother and sister.

As tends to happen in legends, the daughter Branwen grew up as a bit of a good-looker. A passing Irish king stopped by to see her father Llyr, and took a bit of a shine to her. So a big and rather posh wedding party was planned. Loads of wealthy relatives came over from Ireland, all dressed up to the nines. But Efnisien was dead miffed that he weren't the centre of attention. Bored and jealous of all the attention his sister was getting, he slipped round to where the Irish nobles' horses were stabled, then snipped off their manes and tails. This sounds enough to get the Irish men more than a bit narked, but in those days such an act was thought to be a real insult and they got dead nasty over it. After rather a lot of smooth-talking, Llyr managed to calm down his new in-laws but had to give them all new horses, which has got to have set him back a bit.

His son-in-law went off home to Ireland with something of an unusual wedding present. It was a cauldron big enough to put a man inside. And to cap it all, not only was it nigh on as big as a house end, it was a magic cauldron – if the man was dead before he was put in the cauldron he would come back to life. What with a gorgeous new wife and a magic cauldron that would mean any of soldiers slain in battle would come back to fight again, he went back to Ireland dead chuffed.

Some years later Llyr's queen died. By then he'd had enough of living on dry land and he'd rather by far be back living in the sea. So he asked his son, Bran, to take over the kingdom. So Bran tried hard to be a fair and wise king. But he had a world of trouble with the antics of his kid brother. One day Efnisien so got up Bran's nose that he banished him from his lands. All along of this Efnisien went over to Ireland to live with his sister. But he was still tetchy and more than a bit awkward to get on with most of the time. Not long after he had turned up at their castle, someone got his back up and he took out his anger on the magic cauldron and started to smash it into smithereens. But it was the last thing he ever did, because one of the big bits crushed him to death.

But Branwen's husband misunderstood and thought that Efnisien had been sent by Bran to smash the cauldron. He mustered all his soldiers and set out for Bran. When they met there was a great battle. It was a right old carry on! Both

Bran and the Irish king died, along with most of their armies. Bran's dying wish was that his head be buried at the Tower of London, to magically protect the country against invaders. So far as anyone knows it's still there to this day.

All these legends about Llyr and Leir are fairly fanciful. But, if we remember that the River Soar was once called the River Leiore (indeed there is still a village called Leire near the source of the river), and that '-cester' just denotes a Roman town (as in Gloucester, Worcester and the like, or simply Chester) then 'Leire-cester' starts to make sense — the Roman town on the river then known as the Leire. But just to confuse things a little, the Romans themselves knew the city they created as Ratae or Ratae Corieltauvororum (Corieltauvi was the tribal name of the Iron Age people who were in charge in these parts before the Romans turned up).

There's plenty of other examples of legends being invented to 'explain' how places got their names. One of these is about a giant called Bel who boasted to his mates that his horse was so wonderful that it could make it from his home near Mountsorrel to Leicester — a journey of about five miles — in just three big laps. His mates told him not to be so daft, but Bel bet them a large sum of money that he could do it. So the challenge was on. His great horse made three great leaps and made it as far as Belgrave, but the horse died of its exertion and Bel was killed in the bad landing that resulted. This daft ditty recounts what supposed to have happened:

> Mountsorrel he mounted at
> Rothley he rode by
> Wanlip he leaped o'er
> At Birstall he burst his gall
> At Belgrave he was buried at.

Truth be told, Belgrave is a name made up by the Normans which means 'beautiful grove'. But the Anglo-Saxons before them knew the place as Merdegrave, which in the Anglo-Saxon language meant a grove where martens lived. But the Normans thought it sounded like their French word merde which means, let's say, 'excrement'. Fairly predictably, they didn't want to live in a place that they thought was called 'sh*t grove', so changed the name to 'beautiful grove'. Indeed, the real origins of all the place-names mentioned in the ditty have nothing to do with the imaginative little tale. But it's still kinda quaint, nonetheless.

That's enough of these dafter legends, interesting though they might be to some folk. Must get a good night's rest as tomorrow I'm off to see my old friend Ella over at Twyford.

Off to meet an old friend

Chapter 2

Off to meet an old friend

Well, its been quite a while since I was out thisaway. Twyford isn't exactly on my doorstep. Strewth, I'm getting a bit flummoxed about where I supposed to be heading. Is that little cottage Ella's? Looks a bit too scruffy, if you ask me. Oh, aye, from what I can see through the muck on the window, it looks like her furniture. Aye, yes, there's that funny doorknocker of hers, that looks like a frog. Or is it a toad?

Rat-ta-tat-tat-tat

'Who's there?'

'Why, it's me'

'Ey up me duck! En't seen you in ages! Wot brings the likes of you out in this d'rection then?'

' 'Ello Ella! Well, thought I'd make it out before the winter closes in − it's better to share someone else's fireside than sit at home on your own, I reckon.'

'Yea, that's for sure, i'n'it. Come on in, come on in. Put the door too, shall you, and Ay'll meke some tea fer us both.'

'Thank you kindly. Aye, it's nice and roomy in here, isn't it.

'It is that, an' all. Bit difficult to keep warm, though. The damp gets on my chest these days.'

'You've not been bad have you?

'Oh, Ay've bin very badly of a long while. A right ol' carry on it were. I were at my wit's ends. At one time I thought for sure as my 'our were coom. But mustn' complain, yer just gorra gerron wi' it. Ay'm pickin' oop noicely nowadays. 'Ere, did you hear about what 'er up the road got up to?'

'Who you talking about? That Jenny?'

'Well, we don't mention 'er by name in this 'ouse, if yer don't mind. She carries 'ot water wi' 'er wherivver 'er goes, she do!'

'Well, they say she's a rum one.'

'And the rest.'

'So, what's she been up to now then that's got your back up?'

'Well, Ay caught 'er round the back in my yard, poking into a hole she'd made with her stick. "Wot yer scrattin' abait at?" Ay asked 'er, an' told 'er that she ain't no rights to be here. Well, that riled 'er and she got quite nasty ovver it. So Ay said to 'er – an' you know wot an ugly mug she's got – Ay said to 'er, "Beauty's only skin deep, but ugly goes to the bone" and that she could go to blazes.'

'Ah, you should just take scant notice of her.'

'You ain't 'eard the best of it yet! As I were sayin', afta' she'd bin gone, Ay has a poke into the 'ole she med and found this little poppet wot was as she'd med – just a clo'es peg with a bit o' ribbun 'round it, but wi' several pins pressed into it between the 'ead and the legs.'

'Ooh, you beggar! Was it in the ground arsy-versy?'

'Aye, it were the wrong road up, that's for sure.'

'What did you do with it?'

'Well, for a start off Ay as that mad Ay was fit to bust. Anyways, Ay ran it through the candle flame a few times to cleanse it of 'er bad intentions. Then around the next full moon for three nights running I did my best to charm it the way Ay wan'ned it. Not to 'er advantage, like. Then I sneaked into 'er yard and popped it in a 'ole, wrong road up. So there it is, that's 'ow she got her comeuppance. Nivva bin the same since, she 'ent, just one thing after another she's bin off to the chemists abairt.'

'Ey, keep that dark or else folk'll be talkin' about you being like a witch an' all.'

'Aye, well Ay wouldn't the first round these parts, would Ay? They still talk about Ol' Joe. 'E were a right un, the way 'e could fix carts, ploughs − even scythes − so folk coon't use 'em. A right carry on, just so's he didn't 'av to work all day long, just went round tapping up all the farmers fer money so's they'd be on the right side, if you get's my meaning.'

'Aye! But not half as clever as the shepherd's wife who lived in Tilton going on hund'rd 'n' fifty years ago who, in her day, could hex herself right to Tilton Woods in a jiffy.'

'Aye, an' 'er daughter were much of a muchness too, but din' wan' to 'ave any part in such goings on. Think she were more than a bit frit of 'er motha [mother]! Did you hear about the time she were up Tilton Woods and danced round a tree seven times then 'it the tree and med flames come from it? Who'd 'ave thought it? Anyways, she did some kind of spells with her daughter up them woods every Chris'mas Eve till she turn' twen'y-one, so as that she didn' end up as a witch an' all.'

'Sounds a bit like Old Sarah from thereabouts who, so I've heard tell, could flit through the air to Tilton Woods and make blood run from a tree by striking it with her hand. Them were the days. And weren't it around that time that the farmer's wife down the lane from you used to turn herself into a hare so she could keep an eye on the neighbours without no one cottoning on? Met her match when the shepherd's dogs took a fancy to her and she didn't get away fast enough. The bite on her leg was still there when she turned back into being a woman again. And it were so bad that she took right ill and went to bed, and died soon after. But she let on to what she'd been up to before she pegged it so as the Devil wouldn't have her. Least, that's what she hoped.'

'Aye, there's them as tell a similar story 'bout an ol' woman from over at Smeeton Westerby too. But that's nowt. There's a tale going about that early one morning some villagers saw all the witches from Twyford and South Croxton together, a whole gang on 'em. Only the villagers say that they was in the guise of cats, and was floating down the brook in a wooden bowl. So they throws stones at 'em and busted the bowl, so they all fell in the water an' drown'd! Wot a daft story! If folk'll believe that, they'll believe owt!'

'Yes, but trouble is they do believe any old nonsense. Think how many folk got hauled up before the justices in the old days.'

'Yes, but it's my belief as that they brought some of the trouble on themselves. For a start off, if they'd used a bit of common sense before opening their mouths and blabbing, mostly there'd be nowt to prosecute them with.'

'But that don't argue for nothing. Think on how the Earl of Rutland had a run in with that woman and her two daughters what worked for him at Belvoir Castle. Seem to remember the Earl were called Francis and his Lady were Cecilia. She had a daughter, Katherine, by a marriage before as well as the two sons she'd had since she married Francis.'

'Folks say that they was as 'appy as doves. That is, 'till they got the wrong side of that woman.'

17

'That's for sure. Joan Flowers she was called. Doesn't seem most folk had much time for her as she was a bit touched. Bit of chip on her shoulder it seems like, and dead jealous of anyone she thought had better fortune than her. Not just that, right spiteful and malicious and all. No surprise village gossip was that she was a witch and had made a pact with Old Bogey himself. Times that's been said of folk that aren't liked too much!'

> 'You can say that again! And she had a cat by the name of Rutterkin who, so was said, was her familiar spirit.'

'Sometimes it seems like anyone with a cat is likely to be thought a witch. Don't think it was the cat that scared folk though as Joan herself could turn right nasty when roused – not just cussing and swearing as much as a whole army of troops, but she had that scary way of looking that made it look like her eyes were ablaze. And the sort of threats she made about how she would get her revenge would frit anyone enough to make them skinless.'

> 'But it weren' just 'er was it – 'er daughters took after 'er. The younger one, Phillipa she were known as, was reckoned to 'ave the power too. They said she bewitched that lad Thomas Simpson so 'e would live with 'er. Result were 'e couldn' control neither 'is mind or 'is body. I wouldn' know for sure, not as I could tell to, but that's what's bin said. The olda daughter Margaret 'ad most of 'er mother's bad ways too. And she were in the 'abit of 'elping herself to anything that took 'er fancy wot she thought folk wouldn't notice.'

'Sure enough though the Countess got to hear about how much was going missing. But she was a generous sort and, instead of just sending Margaret away she gen her a big sum of money – 40 shillings I think, which were a small fortune then, and a couple of big pillows.'

'But that weren't enough for the ungrateful little hussy 'n' 'er motha 'n' sister. They went over to Blackberry 'ill near the castle and called up Old Boots [the Devil] to get the power to curse the Earl 'n' the Countess. They worked out how to nip off some of their 'air [hair] and cop 'old on a pair o' gloves then ritually burnt the 'air and boiled the gloves, all the while casting a spell to harm the Earl and 'is family.'

'From what was said at their trial I think they did it more than the once, and there were a good few of them involved in these goings on. Didn't it also involve rubbing the glove on the back of that cat Rutterkin, and stabbing the glove with a knife? Certainly the Earl and his Lady went down with a series of strange afflictions around that time. Then their oldest son, Henry, took bad too. Despite the best efforts of the best doctors around, the lad died.'

'Too right, 'n' Joan 'n' 'er gals thought this were all down to them! But they wern' conten'to stop there. They then gorra glove worn by the other son, Francis 'e were called, and did a ritual wot involved boiling it and sticking pins in it.'

'And he were proper poorly too! But not so out of sorts as he died. So they did some stronger magic and buried the glove in a pile of cow clat. Idea was that, as the glove rotted away, so Francis's health would deter'iate till he was a gonner too.'

'And die he did, though it weren't for another seven years, and that's a year or two after Joan and 'er daughters met their end.'

'But before they were had up the spells began to be used against the Countess and her daughter. This time they'd pinched one of her hankies. The daughter took right ill, but the doctor managed to save her.'

'Don't forget they also did spells with fevas [feathers] from the Earl's bed to make sure he and the Countess couldn' 'ave any more children. Weren' the fevas boiled with blud 'n' water, or some such?'

'But folks started talking, as they do, and the Countess got to hear. So the three were had up before the judges about Christmas in 1617, along with three others.'

'Difficult to know 'ow all of them she took up with were involved. Ann Baker came from Bottesford, which is local enough, but Ellen Greene was from Stathern and Joan Willimot lived all the way over at Goadby.'

'Whatever, and don't forget that Joan Flowers was from Langham. Anyways, they all got took up to Lincoln gaol to be put on trial. Then old Joan stood up before the justices and said she was blameless and would prove it by taking bread and water. In them days it was believed that if you were innocent you would swallow it all right, but if you were guilty then God would make you choke to death. Anyways, she put the bread in her mouth and, to the amazement of everyone that was there, she fell down in a fit. She were dead before the doctor could get there.'

'Some say she knew that she wo'n' ger'away [wouldn't get away] with wot she'd been up to so, rather than be 'ung, she'd 'idden some poison in wi' the bread.'

'That's as maybe. It terrified the daughters though and they confessed what they'd been up to. They were hanged on 11th March 1618. The Earl went on to live till 1632, but he never forgot the Flowers women as on his grand tomb in Bottesford church it says "In 1608 he married Lady Cecilia Hungerford by whom he had two sons died in their infancy by wicked practice and sorcery." '

'Only place in England you'll see such an inscription, Ay've bin told.'

'Seems likely, that's for sure, though that's out of my knowledge. But don't forget about that effigy over at

Edmondthorpe, the one to Sir Roger Smith and his two wives. The wrist of one of the wives, Lady Ann, has a red stain and the locals say she was a witch who shape-shifted into a cat.

'They say that she were a real good-looker who had Spanish blood in her, and was a lot younger than her husband. She were well set up! No one would look her in the eyes though, 'cause they thought she could read their most private thoughts, like she had the power. Well, after she came back from a trip to London, she confronted the butler with an accurate account of how, while she'd been away, the servants had been dancing and getting up to other bawdy activities. Now at this time the Puritans had forbidden anything of the sort, so this was quite serious. The butler knew she'd not had the chance to talk to anyone else, so 'e was more than a bit terrified by how she knew.

'Anyways, a short while after the butler was in the kitchen with the cook and telling her how as he'd seen her Ladyship riding her horse at night with only the moonlight to see by. She might have been up to all sorts, the cook suggested. Then, right at that moment, a large black cat leapt from the window ledge right into the butler's face and began scratching him right bad. The cook came over and swiped at the cat with the cleaver she was holding, and gashed its left paw. The cat fled, leaving a trail of blood.

'As the butler served dinner that evening he noticed that Lady Ann had a bandage around her left wrist and was looking very pale. As he began to tell Sir Roger of the strange goings on in the kitchen he caught the Lady's dark eyes. With just one stare he found that his throat had dried up and he couldn't finish the sentence.

'That's unpossible! Seems like a med up story if ever there was!'

'Maybe so, maybe not. The bloodstain on the kitchen floor of Edmondthorpe Hall couldn't be scrubbed away. It was still there about 1920 when the maids complained that it would never come clean and the owner of the Hall got the stone replaced.'

'I've nivver 'eard tell on it before but Ay'll tek your word.'

'In them there times it were the done thing to blame witches for anything untoward. Only a few years before the Belvoir goings-on, in 1616, the king himself, it was James I then, had written a book called Daemonologie which denounced witchcraft.'

'Wern' that the year when nine women were 'anged in Leicester? Ay've got an ol' book 'ere, wi' a letter wri'n at the time by Robert Heyrick to 'is brother William:

We have been greatly busied this four or five days past, being assize time, and a busy assize, especially about a sort of woman, witches, that nine of them shall be executed at the gallows this forenoon for be-witching of a young gentleman of the age of 12 or 13 years old, being the son of one Mr Smith of Husbands Bosworth.

'From what the lad, John, said in court 'e was trying to make out that 'is fits were caused by these women's familiars, in the form of a dog, cat, 'orse, and what might 'ave bin a stoat. The weirdest of these was a couple of fish! Apparently the lad thought 'e was bein' tormented by all these familiar spirits and, dependin' on which one 'e thought was 'aving a go at 'im, 'e would make different noises. So, if it were the 'orse wot was the problem, 'e would whinney.'

'Strange sorts of fits they were too. Look here in your book, there's a description:

Sir Henry Hastings had done what he could to hold him in his fit; but he, and another as strong as he, could not hold him. If he might have his arm at liberty, he would strike himself such blows on his breast, being in his short, that you might hear the sound of it the length of the whole chamber – sometimes fifty blows, sometimes a hundred, yea, sometimes two or three hundred blows, the least of them was able to strike down a strong man; and yet all he did to himself he did no hurt.

'Oi! Look 'ere! It says that later that year King James came to Leicester and was so intrigued by the court records that he interviewed the boy. But he thought the whole thing was a pack of lies, so the poor women had died all for nothing. Thankfully six other women about to be tried for witchcraft by the same justices were released from gaol, except one had already died while she was in there. The book also says that the first person in Leicester we know to be hanged for witchcraft was woman known as Old Mother Cooke, who was accused by a Mr Edward Saunders in 1596.'

'An' it wern' only the women they wos afta. The vicar at Swithland, Gilbert Smith, complained to the justices in Leicester in 1620 that Christopher Monk 'ad said 'e was a sorc'rer and the means of the breaking of 'is wife's arm, 'n' of 'is son's cuttin' of 'is own throat. Shame it don' say anywhere wot becum of 'im.'

'Here's a few other good ones from your book. They're all women, mind. The first was called Agnes Tedsall, who was tried in 1635 for causing the death of Richard Linsey "by witchcraft". But she was let off. In 1650 four townswomen had to examine Ann Chettle to determine if she had a "witch

23

mark". This was the name for any spot which did not bleed when pricked by a needle, so I think we can imagine how distressing that examination must have been. However two years later she was in trouble again, though we don't know what happened to her that time.'

'Seems to be a bit of a gap till we hear of such accusations ag'en. Though around these times folk were digging holes right down underneath the foundations of churches so they could bury glass bottles. These bottles 'ad in 'em bent pins, or 'air, or nail clippin's, and either piss or the sort of oil used for church services in those days. One was found at South Kilworth and a couple of small 'uns at Lutterworth. Presumably someone was tryin' to bewitch the person who's piss or 'air or whatever they 'ad teken. Or might be that it was intended as a way of warding off attacks.

'Anyways accusations of witchcraft started up all ova' ag'in when the parson at 'Ornin'old [Horninghold] who went by the name of 'Umphrey Michel...'

'Reverend Humphrey Michel, please!'

'If yer must. As I were saying, this "Reverend" seems to have got a bit of a cob on about witches and got the locals to start a few duckin's.'

'That's the daft idea that if you sink you're innocent but if you float you're guilty... '

'That seems about right. The "Reverend's" diaries 'ave come down to us and they says that the first such "swimmin'" took place on 11th June 1709, which was Whitsun Eve. Except that it were a bloke who was alleged to have been a witch. 'Is name were Thomas Holt and they took 'im to the next village, Blaston, tied 'is 'ands 'n' feet, then dunked him in a place known as the Dungeon Pit, where he stayed on top of the water. Says there was berra [better] than five

hund'rd people watchin'. Then a week leta [later] the
"Reverend" egged things on ag'en an' a crowd wot
were even bigga watched two old gals bein' chuck'd
into this Pit. There names was Elizabeth Ridgway 'n'
Jane Barlow.'

'They both swam, which by the so-called logic of this
lynching, meant they were guilty of being witches. So Jane
asks to clear her name by being ducked again, but this time in
the Great Close Pond, 'cause she thought that wasn't as
enchanted as Dungeon Pit. So they ducked her again, but
again she swam. The crowd seemed to be having a good time,
so they got hold of another bloke, who said he was innocent
and they could prove that only witches had the power to
swim. This they did and he sank. Not content, the crowd
then set off for Jane's older sister who had been crippled
since birth. She was ducked several times and she also swam.

'Then things went quiet for a couple of months, whereupon
Elizabeth Ridgway becomes the centre of speculation once
more. In his diary, Reverend Michel records for 15th August
that:

> One, Frances Sharp, the wife of Thomas Sharp,
> was buried and was in all probability bewitched to
> death by one, Widow Ridgway, for the other
> confessed that the said Ridgeway appeared to her
> in very terrible shapes and before she died she
> neither ate nor drank of eleven days, but said she
> could have done both very heartily but that the
> little thing in her bosom told her that she must
> do neither, and while the white witch of
> Kibworth, Clow, had ordered a charm to be sewed
> and she kept it in her shift about her bosom she
> did eat and drink, but then when she had scratted
> it away she never ate nor drank more.

' 'Is diary where 'e tells how in October he preached a sermon about the line in the Bible that says 'There shall not be found among you any one that maketh his son or his daughter to pass through the fire, or that useth divination, or an observer, or a witch, or a charmer, or a consulter with familiar spirits, or a wizard, or a necromancer.' One of Jane Barlow's daughters just gorrup an' walked out of the church there and then.'

'But such goings on were going out of fashion. The last secular witchcraft trial anywhere in England took place in Leicester in 1717. Seems one Jane Clarke of Wigston Magna, together with her son and daughter, were ducked – no matter that the Lord Chief Justice himself had warned people against doing this some five years previous. No less than twenty-five people were prepared to testify that they were witches. But the jury took no notice and threw out the case.'

'Din' stop 'em gerrin' up to duckin' folk though! They was still at 'ere in Twyford in 1736, the year that witchcraft were no longer any crime. So the vicar, Joseph Juxon – ahmm, Reverend Joseph Juxon – preached a sermon about these "foolish unwarrantable experiments" and reminded his parishioners that witchcraft had "no other foundation than ignorance or superstition." '

'Aye, but by 1760 the boot was on the other foot and those that ducked supposed witches were punished themselves.'

'That's just what 'appened that year when two women over at Great Glen started arguin' and carryin' on and callin' each other witches an' all that. The locals set up an ordeal by swimmin'. So these poor ol' gals 'ad their thumbs and big toes tied together. Then they was thrown into the middle of the village pond. Just as well they purra [put a] rope around their middles first

26

as one of them sank straight away, although the other floated right enough. 'Er wot they thought was guilty was then asked to say who 'er accomplices were. So she told 'em that several ol' women Burton Overy, wot's nearby, were "as much witches as she was". So the mob went off to Burton 'n' broke into the 'ouse of an ol' woman. They grabbed 'old on 'er an' repeated the duckin' experience wi' 'er. But they couldn' decide w'ither or not she could swim. Anyways, over the next couple a' days two o'ver [other] people were also treated to the same, how do yer wan' to call it, experience, but them ordeals didn' prove they was innocent or not neither.'

'Thankfully news of the mob reached the ears of authorities and the ringleaders were brought before the bench. They didn't get off scot free, mind. Two ended up in the pillory with a month in gaol, and about twenty more were fined for assault.

'It were about then that them from 'ere in Twyford got themselves ducked – one of 'em nearly copped it, too. It were 1775, which makes it about the last time anyone 'ere in Leicestershire was ducked for being a witch, apart from the next year when an ol' woman of eighty was stripped naked and "swum" in front of a jeerin' crowd at Aston Flamville. But people were getting' more h'indignant about such goings on.'

'Didn't stop folk believing in witches though. Over at Elmesthorpe a farmer is on record from 1811 saying how the women make crosses to keep the witches out of the mash tub when they are brewing beer.'

'And over near Caldecott where there used to be a village what was called Snelston, they say as how a witch would hang on to carts' wheels as they struggled up Galley Hill, meking the 'orses work even 'arder. Bit like roun' here at Tilton where word 'ad it if a farmer upset certain women then they would stop the

farmer's plough 'osses in their tracks, or make his
wagg'ns and 'osses stand fixed in the road. Same
way they was said to stop the cows from giving any
milk, or meking it so that the cream wouldn' turn to
burra [butter].'

'So folk kept a "witch stone" in their dairy to forestall any
such goings on. It were nowt but a stone that had a natural
hole through the middle hung up on a thread. One from
Wymeswold was presented to Leicester Museum back in 1852
but hasn't been seen again for many a year. Plenty are known
from elsewhere in the country though.'

> 'Reckon it was the witches from Fleckney who had the
> most going for 'em though! For a start off, nor'only
> did they dress in darkest black but they also carried
> small black bags. These bags was said to have in 'em
> snake's skins, frog's hearts, mole's paws, withered
> belladonna plants and who knows what. They reggler
> [regularly] sat on a seat at the end of the main street.
> It was known as Witches's Seat and only old women
> sat on it. One chap from thereabouts took the mickey
> out of them. One day he was brave enough – or
> perhaps it were daft enough, eh? – to sit on this seat.
> Anyways, soon afterwards one night halfway back from
> the next village his 'oss missed its step and the chap
> landed on the ground with 'is neck busted. Next
> morning the sun came up and folk saw his 'oss
> standing over his body. Word got round that the
> black witches had called up a ghost from Hades to
> torment the night-time traveller.'

'The place were he died then got known as Witchcraft
Corner, though folk were a bit coy and just said "Craft
Corner". When a bloke built a house there he wanted to call
it Craft House but his family wasn't so keen so it got called
Croft House, which it still seems to be today.'

> 'Mustn' forget that not all witches gorra bad

reputation. Remember Amelia Woodcock over at Wing? In the nineteenth century she was right famous as "The Wise Woman of Wing". Put it about that she was the seventh daughter of a seventh daughter.'

'Yes, but despite her strange looks she was a less a witch than a good herbalist. She died fairly young in 1867, but helped countless people during her life.

'Ay 'eard as it were up at Wing that some folk 'ad tried to 'edge in a cuckoo to stop summer from endin'... '

'Oh, that sounds just like one of the better-known 'tales of the "Wise Men" of Gotham up in Nottinghamshire. My aunt, I'd better not start on all that, else I'll be here all night. Though it's interesting to know they tell the same sort of legend in Rutland too. Heck it's getting a bit dark out there. I'd better be nipping off right aways. Thanks for the tea and all. I'll try not to leave it so long before coming over again.'

Weird goings on

Chapter 3

Weird goings on

Must admit these murky old winter evenings don't do much for me. Make me want to sit in my armchair close up against the fire. A spot of whisky in my tea does one the power of good and helps with keeping me feeling warm too. Always keep a little bottle of whisky handy, just in case of emergencies. Not a lot in it at the moment, mind – must have had quite a few 'emergencies' lately, eh?

Truth be told, after a hot toddy or three my mind starts pondering on this and that and won't let go. Last night my thoughts turned to St Wistan. Now there's a fine old legend if ever there was, but seems as if it might have more than a bit of truth about it. But I can never quite tell how true it might have been.

The way it's usually told is that Wistan was the son of Wigmund, one of the Anglo-Saxon kings of the Midlands, at that time known as Mercia. Even though it's spelt 'Wigmund' he would have pronounced his name 'Wymund' – although whether he is the same chap who gave his name to Wymondham and Wymeswold in the north of the county is another matter. More likely a different bloke of the same name.

Anyways, Wistan should have taken over the throne when his father died, but he was more of a religious type, and still quite young. So he asked his mother, Queen Elfleda, to act as regent. Well, this caused all sorts of intrigues in the family – a Dark Age soap opera if ever there were such a thing! Wistan had a cousin, Berhtric, who decided that if he married Elfleda then he would to all intents and purposes be the king. But Wistan understandably thought a marriage between such close relatives was not on. So Berhtric wasn't over-pleased with Wistan. He invited Wistan to a meeting so he could have a few words with him, as it were. Come the meeting, Berhtric suggested they wandered off to a more private spot so they would not be overheard. But this was just a devious ploy and instead of sorting out their differences Berhtric did away with Wistan by hitting him on the head with the hilt of his sword.

He then buried the body before anyone noticed. What's more, he might have got away with it too, except that a column of light appeared above where Wistan's body was buried. Even more weird, hair sprouted from the ground where his blood had run. Berhtric never did take the Mercian throne – instead his feelings of guilt sent him round the twist.

It all seems to fit the facts too as, back in the year 850, one of the king's big estates was being run from Great Glen, the next village to Wistow. This would be just the sort of place where people like Berhtric might arrange to meet other important folk. Indeed a royal charter describing a gift of land has come down to us and that was signed at Glen in the same year Wistan died. It could even have been that everyone had gathered together for a royal court to sort out such administrative things as gifts of land, and it would have been entirely appropriate for Wistan and Berhtirc to have needed to meet up for such an occasion, the go off for a one-to-one chat to try to resolve any tricky problems.

The place where St Wistan was murdered became known as Wistanstow, which originally meant 'Wistan's holy place'. His bones were taken to Repton, by the River Trent in Derbyshire, where the Mercian kings had already built an imposing crypt for their mortal remains – it can still be visited today, although there is no evidence of the kings anymore.

Wistan was soon made into a saint. It was said that where he died nothing grew except grass which sprouted like hair for just one hour on the 1st June, to commemorate the day of his death. This sounds a bit improbable and, indeed, the chap who was Archbishop of Canterbury from 1183 to 1190, called Baldwin, thought it rather unlikely too. So he got a bunch of religious types, including the Abbot of Leicester, to keep watch on the right day. They were more than a bit flabbergasted when they saw the hair grow, though we don't know what the Archbishop had to say for himself when they reported this back to him.

Wistanstow got shortened to 'Wistow', where there is a church dedicated to St Wistan (although for many years misspelled as St Wolstan). The little church there now is not the original, as what stands today is a neat example of eighteenth century architecture (and Leicestershire doesn't have many churches from that time). Frankly, it's a daft place to build a church as it's very easily flooded – most churches are put up on high ground. So it seems quite likely that it is on, or very close to, the site where Wistan was killed. Quite likely too, until Henry VIII nicked any goodies from all the churches, there would have been an elaborate statue of St Wistan in a shrine, probably gilded and perhaps with jewels, and this would have attracted lots of pilgrims, who could easily be persuaded to make lucrative donations that more than covered the upkeep of the church. St Wistan is also commemorated down the road at 'Wigston Two Steeples', where one of the two churches is also dedicated to him.

Some 170 years after Wistan died the Abbot of Evesham asked the king – at this time it was Canute, him what got his feet wet on the beach onetime – to allow Wistan's bones to be taken to Evesham Abbey. So Repton lost out to Evesham. Then, in 1067, just a year after the Norman conquest, a new Abbot was appointed at Evesham, one Walter de Cerisy – so he was clearly a Norman too (which means we can guess that the previous Abbot was none to keen on William the Conqueror and got 'retired'). Walter was a bit of a sceptic and didn't think that St Wistan was all that saintly. So the Bishop decided to put Wistan's sanctity to the test by putting his bones in a fire. However, not only did they not burn, but they were not even blackened. When the Abbot picked up the skull he was so overcome that his hands went all of a tremble and he dropped it, so it smashed to smithereens. Undeterred he wrapped the pieces up in a piece of cloth. Though I bet if anyone asked him how he came to break it, he said what every kid says 'Oh, it weren't me! It just come apart in me hand!'

Later on it wasn't only St Wistan's remains that got a bit smashed up. Come 1207 the tower of the Abbey collapsed, and some masonry fell on his shrine, exposing the skull wrapped up in the Norman cloth. When the monks of Repton heard about this the asked for a fragment of the skull to be returned to them – after all saints' relics were very good for encouraging the tourist, sorry, pilgrimage business. Indeed, a fragment of his head and an arm bone made there way back to Derbyshire, no doubt accompanied by a great deal of pomp and circumstance – a good excuse for lots of smells and bells.

So it seems that until the Reformation pilgrims could venerate St Wistan in at least three places – Wistow, Evesham and Repton. There may also have been some of his remains over in Shropshire where there is a village called Wistanstow, although no historical links have been made between this place and St Wistan.

How come we know so much about this decidely obscure Anglo-Saxon saint? Well, in 1218 a Prior of Evesham, Thomas de Marleberge, wrote an account of his life and that has survived.

If grass sprouting up like hair for an hour seems an unlikely basis on which to build a church, then you haven't heard nothing yet. Along the road in Fleckney the locals decided to build a new church somewhere about a mile west of the middle of the present village. Problem was that each night the 'little folk' threw the stones into the nearby stream. Somehow this stream managed to wash the stones a mile downstream and drop them near to where the church is now.

So the builders decided to heed the wishes of the 'little folk' and take the hint to build it near where the stones had washed up.

Not to be outdone, the folk at the next village of Kibworth also found that the newly-laid stones of their church were moved to where the church is now by a mysterious agency. Same is also said for the church at Tilton on the Hill, a few miles up the road. But the best yarn of all concerns Breedon church over in the west of the county. The church is at the top of a massive hill but the locals originally decided, quite sensibly, that their church should be at the bottom of the hill close to the village. However every night the stones were taken up to the top of the hill by doves! Bet whoever really did have to lug all the masonry up to the top of the hill would have been dead grateful if a bunch of doves had done the job for him! Actually there seems to have been medieval sayings about 'when sparrows build churches on a height' and a variant about 'when wrens carry sacks to the mill', – both of which probably meant the same as 'when pigs can fly' or 'when the cow jumps over the moon' – so I think the Breedon tale is just a local version of these old adages that's been, shall we say, 'embroidered'.

While we're on about Breedon, my favourite tale about that place tells how at one time a good fairy called Hob would help the village women with any housework. However one day one of the women put upon him and he took umbrage – fairy folk seem to have easily been upset – and went off to live in a cave.

And speaking of fairies, that puts me in mind of stories of them living in hollow hills. Not that we've any of those in these parts, but we do have a couple of Piper's Holes which are near as dash it the same sort of thing. The best known Piper's Hole is on the ironstone ridge along from Long Clawson on the boundary between Eastwell and Hose – there's still a farm called Piper's Hole Farm up on the top. This Piper's Hole is more like a cleft in the ridge. Back at the end of the eighteenth century the antiquarian John Nichols described it as 'A woody secreted spot, beautifully situated.' He went on to say that 'Here, tradition says, dwelt the professors of a religious institution,' although there's no other evidence for that.

In other parts of Britain piper's holes are not really physical holes in the ground. Instead, they are associated with supernatural entrances to the fairy world, rather as the Pied Piper of Hamelin led all the children into a hill. No such folklore has been recorded in Leicestershire, but the stories from elsewhere usually tell of how a musician – often a piper but sometimes a fiddler – would be intrigued by such an underworld entrance. To find out where it went he'd agree to go into the entrance and continue playing, so that his friends on the ground above could follow the sound of his instrument and hear where he'd got to. Usually the musician is accompanied by his dog. Anyway, according to these tales all goes well until suddenly the music stops. Minutes later the dog emerges, its hair all on end and clearly scared near to death. The musician is never seen again but, on certain nights of the year, the sound of his instrument can still be heard.

There's a really similar tale told only a few years back about an old man who once lived in Hathern. Most nights he walked to his favourite inn in Shepshed where he entertained the house on his pipe. Afterwards he would make his way home, following a path through the woods and playing his pipe as he went. One night he left the inn, but never got home. Despite searches being made he was never seen again.

But for years after different people, even those new to the area, would ask about who played strange tunes on a pipe in the wood. So the wood got known as Pipers Wood. The M1 motorway destroyed most of the wood, so the piper has been drowned out by all the heavy trucks and fast cars. However it may as be that that this recent account is a watered down version of the usual 'piper's hole' tale and the wood may once have been known as Piper's Hole Wood.

Even more tantalising is a brief reference to another Piper's

Hole at Griffydam, a few miles to the west of Hathern. But then Griffydam's got it's own daft legend too. The story goes that an old well at the side of the road got taken over by a griffin – a mythical beastie with the bottom half of a lion and the top half of an eagle. The villagers were a bit put out because this meant they had to walk two miles to the next village to get water. Anyway, one day a knight comes by and asks for water for himself and his horse. When he hears the problem he obligingly went along and put an arrow straight through the beastie's neck – though don't ask me why the villages couldn't have done this themselves anyway, suppose it just makes a slightly better tale. Seems quite likely someone's imagination ran away with them and thought the name Griffydam had something to do with griffins, which it doesn't, it's a corruption of "Griffiths' Dam", though no one seem to know who Mr Griffiths was.

Must be time to mash some more tea, all this remembering malarkey is making me thirsty. Oh! My Gad! The fire's near gone out and all!

Shivers down the back of the neck

Chapter 4

Shivers down the back of the neck

Rat-ta-tat-tat-tat

Who's that at the door this time of night? Only just put the cat out, it'll be trying to sneak back in now.

'Oh hello, fancy you turning out this time of night, Ethel. Everything alright?'

> 'Oh I suppose so. But just near enough frit meself to death down the lane. It's made all the back of me neck go funny, and me knees are all shekky, like. I'm all of a dither.'

'What sort of fright? Come on in, come on in.'

> 'Oh thank you ever so duck. Knew you'd be the person who I could turn to, like. It weren' anybody trying to, you know, take advantage of me or anything like that. In fact I don' know wot it were – just like a shape at the side of the lane and I just went over all queer. Never knew there were a ghost round these parts. Not sure I even believe in ghosts, really, but if there are such things about then that must 'ave bin one.'

']ust you sit yourself down and settle down a bit. I'll just mash some tea for us.'

> 'Oh that's very kind, thank you, thank you very much.'

Well we settled down and took her mind off things. Then, all of a moment, Ethel says to me 'It must 'ave been John O'Gaunt who come ag'en!'

'Who was?'

> 'Same as Ay just sed – that bogey wot I saw jus' now.
> They say 'is ghost 'aunts the Cas'le and that's more or
> less where I were. 'E were dressed all old fashion'
> like, and in a crack 'e were gone. Just went straight
> through the door of the church – the little door near
> the Castle Green – without opening it or anything.
> That's wot were real frigh'nin'. And they say it's the
> ghost of John O'Gaunt who's seen round there. So it
> must be as 'im who's come ag'en. What do you think
> to it?'

'Oh well there's plenty of ghosts round that part of town,
that's for sure. Not sure why it needs be John O'Gaunt,
even though folks think the cellars of the castle were built by
him back in the fourteenth century. Strikes me ghosts always
have to someone rich and famous, so they've got a bit of
romance about them. They're never just your ordinary hoi
polloi wandering about doing nothing very special. It's like
there needs to be a bit of story about why they're seen where
they are, almost as if they were actors on a kind of
supernatural stage.

> 'Oh well now, that's getting a bit philosophical, in'it,
> for this time of the night? You've bin too much
> readin', you 'ave.'

'Well, thinking about it, I suppose it's not surprising that
area's a bit eerie given that the Castle Green is where they
executed people who had been up before the courts in the
Castle. But having said that, the ghost most folk see round
there is a Victorian gent complete with top hat. They say it's
an historian from back then called William Napier Reeve.
When he was still with us he was very fond of sitting quietly
in that area and, after his death, they say he couldn't keep
away. Though last time he's been seen, at least to my
knowledge, was in 1981, so perhaps he's found somewhere
else to while away eternity.

'Folk also tell of a how a boy used to be followed by footsteps all the way from Friar Lane but then the footsteps stopped every time he got to St Mary de Castro. Only once did he see anything. It was Midsummer's Eve and he saw on the ground beside him the shadow that looked like a headless man with a humped back, or something on his back in a sack. The shadow stayed with him all the way to St Mary's when it went off to the main door and just disappeared.

'I don't say I believe in any of this, but there's the really famous ghost of an old lady who lots of people saw in a house in the Newarke. Funny thing about her was that she was always wearing a red coat. Not been seen for well over an hundred years though.'

'Perhaps they got the clergy in to exercise it? You know, with the bell, book and candle and all that.'

'Yes there's been plenty of that going on, though I think you mean "exorcise". No surprise that folk don't see ghosts any more, they've all been "moved on" as if they were like beggars, or gypsies, or asylum seekers, or such. At this rate, one day soon there will be no ghosts left around. Don't know where they've all moved on to, mind.'

'Well by all good rights they should be moved! Can't have them mekin' people like me frit all the time! I remember that poor chap Mr Harris who was serving in a bar at the Freewheeler Club when it opened in Chuchg't early in the seventies. 'E says 'e were near frightened out of 'is life when 'e saw this ol' man dressed all posh with a long frock coat, a cravat and both 'is 'ands restin' on a walkin' stick. 'E had a beard an' what looked like an evil expression on his face. This old man appeared to 'im several times when 'e was upstairs. And 'e also saw the ghost of a li'l gal downstairs where the club was. When folk told 'im that when the place was built in the nineteenth century it 'ad once been used as a mortu'ry then he went off and got the vicar and 'ad the place exercised, er, exorcised.'

'Wonder if that was the same clergy who turned up at the Britella factory on Frog Island about that time? All the Mercury said was that there had been a series of terrifying apparitions and disturbing events there. Things got so bad that the factory was exorcised by no less than the Archdeacon of Loughborough.'

> 'Last time I saw a ghost was over at Newton
> Burgoland. Well, I didn't see him but I felt him, like.
> I was standing in the Belper Inn one afternoon and all
> of a sudden I felt someone pinch my bottom, right
> hard. I turned around to belt him one, but there was
> no one there. I asked the person I was with who it
> were wot 'ad passed me, but they looked at me kinda
> queer and said no one else 'ad been near us. Then
> the landlord chipped in and said "That were Five t'
> Four Fred – 'e's been doin' that fer years, always this
> time a day." And do yer know, it must have bin
> exac'ly five t' four when 'e pinched me bum!
> Landlord then said it's the ladies 'e pinches "fondly" or
> caresses their faces, whereas men feel as if 'e's
> smothering their mouths – 'e's bin known to half
> suffocate one chap who tried to sleep in the bar
> overnight. And 'e's a right pain for movin' things
> about when no one's lookin'.'

'Aye, but when the landlord changed in 1970 not a lot more was heard – or felt – about Five to Four Fred. There's possibly something in it all, though it strikes me that rather too many pubs say they've got some quirky supernatural "residents". Seems more likely it's a bit of good publicity. You can't imagine the landlords having the premises exorcised – more likely if a member of the clergy turned up with his bible and holy water they'd chuck him out head first into the street rather than lose their customers intrigued by the thought of a "spiritual" encounter.'

'Yes but some of them spirits seem to have become real reg'lars. Not long after John and Beryl Messer took over the Woodman's Stroke at Rothley – think it were in 1970 – Beryl was there alone one mornin'. She becem' aware of a big fella, very tall with gaunt features and dressed in dark clothes. She said to 'im "I'm terribly sorry, but we're closed." Then the figure vanished and Beryl realised the main door was still locked shut. Once she'd got over that initial fright it seems they got used to 'im being aroun' and they called 'im "Gregory". 'E mekes a bit of noise stampin' around upstairs, throws stools about, turns taps on and occasionally mekes 'imself seen or felt. But seems 'e's not too much of a nuisance. Indeed she thought 'e tried to reassure 'er at the time 'er son Stephen was right ill in 'ospit'l. But then when Stephen left to get marri'd 'e gor'right upset and hurled stools and other stuff about the place.

'The buildin's right old, and was once used as an undertekers, but some of the locals think it's the ghost of a chap who lived there before goin' off to fight in the Fu'st Wurld War but niver come back.'

'Wonder if your Gregory is the same as the ghost that's been seen at the old Railway station at Rothley? It's a bit of a stroll from the pub but if you've been cooped up in an old inn all those years perhaps you need to stretch your legs from time to time.'

'Gerron with yer! You ain't tekin' me serious, you in't!'

'Well Ethel, all I'll say is it's a good job you don't live along the road from Loughborough to Ashby de la Zouch, the one they now call the A512. Seems there's a ghost in near enough every building nearby, although the nice couple who found out about them haven't told many folk about it all. Seem to recall that one of the places is another pub, the

Drum and Monkey at Thringstone. It's said to be haunted by the ghost of a victim of a murder committed there.

'But there's no doubt that the ruins of Grace Dieu Priory are haunted by the ghost of a white lady. Once, in the 1960s, a bus stopped to pick her up, whereupon she promptly vanished! Both the bus driver and the conductor saw her.

'Kind of fits in with the history of the place too. This priory was built as an Augustinian nunnery and these nuns were known as the "White Nuns" because of their distinctive coloured habits. At the time of the Dissolution in the 1530s the prioress fled from King Henry VIII's men, taking with her – so it's said – many valuable relics. The story goes that after burying the treasure she then tried to escape by a secret tunnel to Ashby de la Zouch castle, improbable as that sounds as the castle is four miles away. The prioress was discovered and killed when she refused to disclose the location of the treasure. Ever since, they say, her ghostly spirit has haunted the ruins. As the prioress at the time of the Dissolution was an Agnes Litherland and she was the only nun who did not receive a pension afterwards, it may just be that she was murdered.

'A gardener who worked there for about forty years got quite used to seeing her apparition. He said she was dressed in white and wore a big hat with a wide brim.

'Some other strange events have been reported, including a policeman who parked his patrol car nearby, I think in the 1980s. When he looked in the rear-view mirror there was a hooded monk sitting on the rear seat. He made a right fast exit! Even more surprising was an event during a trial being held in the grounds many years ago. One of the defendants claimed his innocence by saying that if he were lying the ground should open and swallow him up. Rather to everyone's surprise, it did! The judge ruled that this had no bearing on the case and dismissed the charge. Later it was discovered that there are old coal seams in the area and so subsidence might account for the physical event – if not for its timing!

'Ey, you should write a book about all these ghosts and supernatural stuff.'

'Oh, there's more than a book's worth of these tales. One day I might get round to it.'

> 'Oh you gorra, yer 'ave! Yer know as 'ow folk like tales wot mek 'em frit, and them's all good uns, them are. Yer'd berra gerron wirrit though, in case there's them that might do it instead, like.'

'Oh Ethel, there's plenty of better things to be doing with your life than spending time writing books. Can you manage another cup of tea?'

> 'Oh, I think I can that.'

Phantom hounds

Chapter 5

Phantom hounds

One of the strangest things that's ever happened to me was when I was over at Leicester Forest late one night. The landlord of the pub I'd been in had told me how some unpleasant characters had been making a damnation nuisance of themselves in recent weeks, helping themselves from peoples' houses when no one was looking and robbing folk who were out and about late at night. Well, it takes more than talk of 'unpleasant characters' to put me off – folks have probably said worse about me in my time. Anyways, I was best part of a mile down the road when I became aware of muffled footsteps behind me and what seemed to be sound of a couple of blokes, or maybe more, talking quietly as they walked along. It was dark enough that I couldn't see nowt of them, and whoever it were wasn't carrying any lanterns or anything like. So I quicken my step a little and kept on moving.

Just about then I became aware of this right big dog a few yards away walking alongside me. Well I call it a dog but it was bigger than any dog I've ever seen before or since. More like the size of a new-born calf. And it was black. Really black, like it was even blacker than the night, though I know that don't make sense really. And the weirdest of all was the way its eyes shone red. Big red eyes that turned to look at me – and I mean big, they could have been saucers. But though it appeared out of nowhere, and was immense, and seriously weird looking, not for a moment did I feel frightened of it. And that's almost the weirdest thing of all, 'cause I'm not that keen on dogs, even titchy ones – and this beast could have turned right nasty without me being able to do anything about it.

Well this hound and I kept going along together, him never more than a few yards away, and me feeling quite secure with him around. In fact I never really thought much more about those blokes I thought I'd heard creeping up on me. The dog and I keeps on walking, almost sociably. There wasn't a soul about, none but the dog, till we gets to where the first of the cottages are, with a few lights still shining in the windows. And then dog just went! Like he'd melted through the hedge or something, 'cause there wasn't any field gates along that stretch. Strewth, it was weird, but if I'm ever out that way and see him again I'll say a big 'thank you'.

Some years later I was recounting this tale and they said that other folk had seen that phantom hound around Leicester Forest and even as far over as Narborough, but that it was a portent of impending disaster. Well can't say I suffered any disaster after seeing it, far from it. Another of these fateful black dogs, with the same blazing eyes, was seen quite often until the 1930s around Back Lane in Birstall – though it's all been built on and this bit is known now as Kilby Avenue. Locals said he lived in a pit round there – they even called it Shag Dog Pit. Long since been filled in. Said to be wild looking, a bit like a big mastiff, but with luminous open jaws 'like dying coals in a dark room' and eyes that glowed with an 'unearthly light'. It was in the habit of following people along the lane, then disappearing. No one seemed that frit of it though, indeed one night is saved a little gal from being accosted by frightening off her would-be attacker, so it seems it had at least something in common with my canine companion. Both as cunning as a Christian, as they used to say.

Seems such phantom hounds have been around for some time too. Good old John Nichols, who included a certain amount of what we now call folklore in his books about the history of Leicestershire – which is kind of impressive, because not many people were taking an interest in such things back then – tells of a black dog seen in 1806. The man was walking from Stoney Stanton to Sapcote. It was a fine night and, according to Nichols, his mind was 'anxiously engaged upon a problem in mathematics' – as you do, eh? He was about eighty yards from Scholar's Bridge when he heard 'a groaning sort of noise' which he could not explain and alarmed him. Not surprising, as that bridge already had a bit of reputation for supernatural goings-on. Indeed, not so far away is Mill Hill where the fairies were said to come out to dance – old Nichols says that the locals told many 'wonderful, traditional tales' about them even in his day. Anyway, this mathematically-inclined chap had just got to the stile close by the bridge and put his foot on the stone at the base when an animal, larger than a fox, which he took to be a 'shagged dog', brushed by his right shoulder at 'a surprising velocity'. Weird thing was he never saw the animal on the ground, but only while it was in mid-air, after which it was lost in the darkness. It was enough to give him the dithers.

Anyway, apart from a bit of a fright it seems he was none the worse for his nocturnal encounter. Which is more than can be said for folks who happen upon the black dog of Holwell Mouth, up above Ab Kettleby on the way to Holwell village. Now this is dead overgrown these days but was once a very pleasant bluebell wood that dropped down steeply to form a semicircular dell with a spring of water coming out of the centre. The water is very iron rich so the whole of the stream bed is a bright rusty colour – looks quite impressive. Back in the eighteenth century the local gentry built a stone arch and seats so they could enjoy picnics there in comfort, but no sign of anything so posh now – just a lot of brambles and nettles!

All the while, though it might be rather pretty in the daytime, seems its not a good idea to be in those parts after dark, 'cause a large black dog is seen there, but only between dusk and dawn. He's said to be at least the size of big black Alsatian, perhaps as big as a wolf. However, there's a lady born around the beginning of the twentieth century who'd lived in those parts for all her life – and she was about eighty at the time – who told one of those folklorists that whenever this black dog appears then there will be an unexpected death in the locality. Not necessarily someone in their family, but someone they know.

She gave a few for instances. Like when a courting couple (seems that this little dell was a favourite spot for such goings on) where there in the 1930s. They say this dog and came back home to find the girl's father had been trampled to death by his own horse. Must have been awful! Then in the 1940s, during the Second World War, a woman went on a picnic to Holwell Mouth with her children. They stayed a bit longer than they planned and it was beginning to get dusk. The dog – larger than any dog she'd ever seen – appeared and started snarling at them. Then, less than two weeks later, she got a letter to say that her husband had been killed in action.

This old woman's grandmother had talked about it too, and called it the Black Shug, and said it used to roam all over the place. However by the twentieth century it seemed only to appear at Holwell Mouth. Seems it hasn't been seen much, if at all, since the 1970s – but the old girl says she feels it's still around and strongly advised folk not to be around Holwell Mouth after dark.

These days reports are more likely to be of what they call 'alien big cats' – 'ABCs' for short – which have nothing to do with aliens from outer space but are the likes of pumas and other exotic cats which aren't native to this country. Seems there's a few seen in different parts of Leicestershire each year. If you ask me, there's likely nothing very supernatural about them. Far more conceivably that they're fancy pets that have been released into the wild when they got too much of a handful for their owners. Seems as if pumas can get by in this part of world by eating rabbits and such like, and they're the sort of animals that would keep themselves to themselves if they heard any humans about, so not many folks would get sight of them. And, just maybe, they've crossbred with other feral felines. Not seen their likes myself, but seems a fair few folk have.

Silent sentinels tell their tales

Chapter 6

Silent sentinels tell their tales

'Oh hello again Ethel. Everything all right this time?'

'Ey up m'duck! Aye, Ay'm fit as a fiddle. It's a nice day, in'it?'

'It is that.'

'You in an 'urry?'

'Well, I was expect Elsie to pop round, but I've about given up on her.'

'Well Ay won' be stoppin' fer long. Just thought you'd be able to answer a question that me gran'son asked me. 'E was doin' some 'istory 'omewuk and 'e came across this picture of the Sain' John's Stone. Seems it stood near Leicester Abbey but 'as long since gone. 'E wanted to know where it wos. Didn't know meself, but Ay told 'im Ay thought you might.'

'Isn't that's the one where they lit bonfires on Midsummer's Eve? That was also the old feast day of St John, which is presumably how the stone gets its name. And then, so they say, after dark on Midsummer's Eve the fairies came out to dance so the children had to make themselves scarce. All sounds a bit romantic till you remember that in those days fairies weren't nice small things with gossamer wings – that's just a load of tosh made up by the Victorians to keep their kiddies amused – but as big as you and I, and bad tempered and cantankerous with it. Not a lot to chose between the fairies and the witches in them days! I'd certainly want to be out their way if they wanted to come out and have a dance.

'To the best of my memory that stone was about six or seven feet high, in the centre of a hollow that was like a natural amphitheatre. But I can't remember it being there after about 1840. Some say it was a natural pillar of sandstone rather than a megalith that had been erected. If it was a natural pillar it would be like the Hemlock Stone near Nottingham, which is also a pillar that seems to have been left when the stone around it was quarried away.'

'Is there anything left of it at all now?'

' No, the area's been built on – it must have stood where the back gardens of Minster Crescent and Avebury Avenue are now. But we know what it looked like because a couple of artists did drawings of it, the last one in 1814.

'Aye, that'll be the one our lad saw.'

'It was in a book by William Kelly, which came out in 1815. From what he says the stone was already in bad shape by then. Seems it was being rubbed away by people visiting it and taking some of the dust away for luck or such like.'

'Wot, they was just rubbin' stuff off of it? Enough to make a bleddeh great stone disappear?

'Seems that way. Kelly also suggests that the stone stood in an ancient grove. This is what he wrote:

Nor should we fail to gaze with profane eyes upon the mysteries of that once sacred spot, with its now desecrated and shattered monolith, where – surrounded by the shade of gigantic oaks – it's verdant encircling slopes, covered...

'Oh, that's all a bit poetical, in'it? 'Ard to imagine now there's 'ouses all ova that part of town.'

'Well no one ever said progress had to be for the better. If your lad wants to see a megalith for himself, he'd better head off towards the ridge above Humberstone where there's a massive stone – it's a whopper said to weigh over twenty tons. Not that you'll see all of it as it's mostly buried in the ground. Still the top of it is there for all to see. It's quite deeply weathered into grooves – one chap has likened it to a brain.

'Oh – so that's 'ow 'Umberstun village gets its name?'

'Maybe, or Humbert's Stone – that's how the village's name was first spelt – may have been a different stone nearer the village but what's now gone. I say that because until recent years the stone that has survived was always known as either the Hoston or the Hellstone, though some local folk called it the Holy Stone. Calling it both the "Hellstone" or "Holy Stone" ain't daft as it might sound, 'cause the Old English word hela meant 'holy'.

'Like St John's Stone, folks said it was unwise to be there after dark as otherwise you might meet up with a fairy. Indeed one chap heard a deep groaning coming from the stone and ran away fast, 'cause he felt sure that one of the fairies was about to appear. The most fancy bit of folklore about it says that there was a nunnery there – though there's no archaeological or historical evidence for anything of the sort – and an underground tunnel all the way to Leicester Abbey about three miles away.'

'And the Druids worshipped there too!'

'Well, let's just say that eighteenth century antiquarians were a bit dotty about Druidical sites and both the Humberstone and St John's Stone were made out to be places where the Druids had worshipped. And a couple of places up in Charnwood Forest – there was said to be an Altar Stone, no less, on Long Buck Hill near the Outwoods, and another such Altar Stone to the south of Mount Saint Bernard's Abbey. That one's still there if you know where to go and looks for all the world like a very useful picnic table, just the sort of thing that would have been put up by the local gentry in about the eighteenth century. Then along comes a fanciful antiquarian a few years later and, lo and behold, it's an altar that's been there for two thousand years! Problem is no one knows very much about where and how the Druids did worship, though it seems unlikely they were in the least bit interested in standing stones and the like.

'It's like a couple of really big standing stones up at Charnwood – one in a wood near the Newtown Linford car park for Bradgate Park and the other right by the side of the Scout camp up on Cat Hill Wood. They're both around eight feet tall. Anywhere else in the country and folk would say they were prehistoric but, in these parts, there just aren't any ancient stones of that sort of size. Given where they are I can't help but feel that a bunch of Boy Scouts back in the 1920s or thereabouts decided to set themselves a challenge and get hold a these stones and stand them upright. Not that anyone's ever come forward to tell me that they remember doing any such thing, mind!'

'Oh... But the Humberstone certainly seems to have been a big bugga! Wot were the height on'it?'

'Seems as if was more of a massive boulder than an upright stone. Until the 1750s it stood in a hollow but then the hollow was filled in. Some geologists dug it up again in 1878 and the local folklorist of the time took measurements which suggest it was about nine feet high and over seven feet wide. Since then it's been almost completely buried, though a few years since a timber-lined hollow was made to reveal a little more of the top part.'

'But wer'n't it supposed t'be unlucky to tamper wi' the stone?'

'So they say. Best evidence to support this notion is that towards the end of the eighteenth century – this is after it had been buried, remember – the prosperous landowner had the top of the stone broken off so as he could plough over it. Well he never prospered again. Indeed, six years later he died in the workhouse, a penniless pauper. At least this story about bad luck meant that when they put a dual carriageway past the side of it the planners and contractors didn't mess with it – it ended up fenced off to the side of a roundabout.

'Not that such stories about bad luck befalling on those who tamper with standing stones did much to help the Moody Bush Stone over between Syston and South Crows'on [Croxton]. It used to stand in a pasture field – all the old ridge and furrow was very clear. It was a nice looking stone, about four feet above ground and five-sided. If you ignored the hedges – which wouldn't have been there when the stone was put up – then there are good views in all directions. I was out that way in the late 1980s with a couple of friends. The landowner came over to see what we was up to – not that he was at all unpleasant or anything. We got chatting and he said to me that he'd heard it was unlucky to mess about with standing stones, so I told him the tale of the Humberstone, then he wandered off. Well he obviously wasn't the superstitious sort 'cause next time I went past the field had been ploughed and there was no sign of the Moody Bush Stone.'

'Wot yer mean, it's just gone... '

'Well it's probably still around somewhere, probably in his garden rockery or somewhere where no one knows about.'

' 'Ow would yer know it if yer saw it ag'en?'

'No problem – it's got the words 'Moody Bush' carved into it!'

'Woz thar'all abairt then? Ay've neva 'eard on a bush getting moody.'

'No, yer daft 'ap'orth! It's from the old word 'moot' which meant a meeting, usually one to sort out matters relating to how the farming and such like was to be organised. So, once upon a time, folk would have come together for a 'moot' at a distinctive bush. Presumably the bush died, or wasn't distinctive enough, or whatever, so they put this standing stone up there as well. However, they way things go folk forgot the word 'moot' and it changed into 'moody'. That must have before the eighteenth century, 'cause the style of lettering used to carve the words 'Moody Bush' seems to date from about then.'

'You'd have thought they'd have got together somewhere warmer like a pub or sum'at.'

'Seems there was a long tradition for such moots to be held out of doors, as folk felt that anywhere indoors could be more easily enchanted. We know that when the moot took place at the Moody Bush Stone then people had to bring a turf from their own part of the land and lay it on top of the stone. Only when all the turfs were in place could the moot start. That's a tradition that could date all the way back to Anglo-Saxon times, cause there's charms from back then that refer to similarly symbolical use of turfs. Some say that it was the one-time owner of estates around Mountsorrel who organised the meetings – moots – there, but I'd reckon there is a good chance that it was once the meeting place for the whole of that part of the county to the north-east of Leicester, which was once known as the Goscote Hundred. Though it might have become a more local moot in later centuries.

'Plenty of other stones were used as meeting places. There was one in the Main Street at Thringstone – it's long since gone now – that was known as the Council Stone. And there is still a distinctive stone known as the Blue Stone at Rearsby – and it really does look rather blue, especially when its wet – that was the customary place to get together to share views and opinions.'

'Aye, folk will always find an excuse to banter. When I was a nipper all the men used to sit around in the cobbler's workshop, talking about politics and gen'r'lly puttin' the world to rights. That was at Asfordby. Well, what do you know, that ol' cobbler's gran'daughter turned out to be none other the Iron Lady 'erself, ol' Maggie Thatcher! She used to get her leg pulled about being the Grantham grocer's daughter, but no one twigged that 'er gran'pa was nowt better than a cobbler! But no wonder she was so keen on becoming a politicians – talking a load of nonsense all day was obviously in 'er blood.'

'Now, now, what you got it for her about?'

'Giz us a break! 'Ow long 'ave yer got?'

'All right, all right, another time.'

'Should have strung 'er up from one of the 'angin' stones in these parts.'

'Now be said! Anyway, they weren't that sort of hanging stone.'

'Wotjer mean? Wot otha sort of 'angin' stone is there?'

'The ones you mean – the ones at Oaks in Charnwood, in what's now the nature reserve, and one that used to be at Beaumanor near Woodhouse, where there's a golf course ... '

'Yeh, that's them.'

'Only the Beaumanor one fell down in 1791, just a few weeks after the historian John Throsby had stood underneath it then done some sketches of it.'

'Yea, but why are they called 'angin' stones if they ain't 'angin' stones?'

'Well they are hanging stones, but in the sense that they're stones what are perched precariously on top of another rock. It's the same way Stonehenge got its name – the "henge" bit means that the stones around the top, the lintels, are "hanging".

'Oh, Ay gerrit. 'Angin' like they're suspended...'

'That's it. The stones are hanging, not someone hanging from the stones. Only there's another stone up at Charnwood where they say a poacher really were accidentally hanged.'

'Nivver 'eard tell o' no such a thing!'

'It's a nice little stone, about four foot high, which stands near a little oak wood on the north-eastern edge of Charnwood Forest. Looking over from the wood at the stone then Ives Head is in the background, with its curious double-peak shape. If you walk a few yards away to the edge of the hilltop you look over the motorway to Loughborough. Until a few years back a big oak tree stood alongside, but that blew down in the wind. It's known as the Grey Hangman Stone. The story goes that one night a chap from Shepshed – back then the folk there were well-known as poachers – was out with the intention of rustling one of the deer. Some say his name was John of Oxley. Well his luck was in and he caught a belter. So as he could carry it a bit better he tied its feet together before picking it up. Seems as most of the weight of the deer was on his shoulders, but the feet were in front of his throat.

'Well problem was he'd had to go quite a way from home before he caught it, so it was a long way back and he was beginning to get knackered. So he got as far as this stone and decided to stop for a breather. He rested the weight of the deer on the stone. Back home his wife got worried. First she thought that the gamekeepers had nabbed her husband. But time passed and there was no word of that. Well, so they say, it was all of two days before a swineherd was up above Lubcloud Farm and saw this figure standing by the stone. He called over but got no reply, so he investigated and found the poor chap was dead because the deer had slipped and trapped his neck, so he was strangled to death.'

'Never! Worra way t'go!'

'Someone even wrote quite a long bit of verse about it all. Problem is that there's about thirty other Hangman Stones in the country and all of them seem to have the same legend. Well, more or less the same, as in most cases it's a sheep that the man's carrying, but a deer would be more likely up on Charnwood.'

'That's right odd. ' Ow come the same legend crops up so often? Can't imagine it's true for all of them stones.'

'Neither can I. So I doubt if it's true for the Grey Hangman one either.'

'Oh you're a right old sceptical, you are.'

'Well, folk do make a load of nonsense out of all this folklore. Not that it's always that easy to prove or disprove. If you're into the idea of leys – what some folk call ley lines, where ancient sites are all lined up dead accurately – then the stone by Gynsill Lane in Anstey is a good example as it is on such a ley that runs from Frog Island, through the stone, through the tower of Anstey church, up through the centre of a natural hill notch where the trees now grow alongside Old John, then on to a well-preserved Iron Age settlement site up above Belton. If you stand at the Gynsill Lane stone you can easily see the church and the hill notch, all neatly lined up. Now this is quite rare, 'cause there's very few places where the different places on such leys can be seen together, and usually it's only one other at most.'

'Isn't that where they put in the western bypass a few years back?'

'Oh yes – and I even think the road was moved a bit to make sure the standing stone wasn't affected. Seem to remember a piece about in the Mercury where the headline suggested making a 'ley by' – gerrit? – so folk could stop and look at it.'

'Y've got me 'ead buzzin' with all these ol' tales. Yer g'in me too much ter remember. Ay'll neva tell 'em all again fer our lad.'

'Well don't forget to tell him about the Wishing Stone.'

'Where's that then?'

'It's in Bradgate Park, just along the path from the Newtown Linford car park, after you've come past where the stream runs through a little gorge – what's laughingly called "Little Cheddar" – to about halfway to the ruins of the old house. You need to climb up and sit on it, then make a wish. It will come true but only if you don't tell anyone what you wished for. Was a time when school kids on outings queued up to make their wishes.'

'Oh, I'll be tekin' im off there soon enough – there's a good few things he should be wishing for, if you ask me. Like givin' me the patience of a saint to put up wi' 'im most days.'

Watch the skies

Chapter 7

Watch the skies

'Can you manage another cup of tea, Ethel?'

　'Oh well I won't say no. Must be going soon though.'

'Oh, there's no rush. Not planning on doing very much later on.'

　'Was it you wot was with me when we saw them lights above Bradg't Park?'

'No, that weren't me. Was that the time just before the big earthquake – well the biggest round these parts since they started keeping records?'

　'I think it might have been. Must have been late fifties as it was before our Bert died.'

'Well the earthquake was on February 11th in 1957, if that helps. Remember everything was shaking all over.'

　'Aye, well that could have been it then.'

'Though there was another earthquake almost a year later, on February 9th, but that wasn't as severe. What did they look like?'

　'Wot did who look like? Ay jest said Ay couldn' remember who I were with, so Ay ain't goin' to be rememberin' wot they as looked like now am Ay?'

'No, "they", the lights in the sky... '

　'Oh, right. Well, just like they was goin' in straight lines.'

'Oh. Not like giant tadpoles or anything?'

'No, don't be daft – wot do yer tek me for, eh? I weren' born yestadey, yer know. It's a poor ol'd doin's when you're being nice as pie and then you get accused of being soft in the 'ead, or summat wurs. I ain't... '

'Alright! No need to get up your high horse, Ethel. Don't start an argy bargy about it. Just that folk have said that's what they saw at that time.'

'Oh. Well, I've neva 'eard tell o' no such a thing myself. Whopping gret tadpoles in the 'eavens! That would be dead odd! Suppose you're going to tell me they glowed an' all...

'More than glowed! They were quite bright...

'Nevva! No, same as I said, I've neva seen anythin' as odd as that. Though them lights going straight out across the sky an' all seemed odd enough t' me. It's still like as I seen 'em yestadey.'

'Seems as its as if the lights are caused by the rocks building up pressure deep underground and, just before everything slips and the earthquake happens, these lights somehow appear, though no one knows quite how or why. Since then people have seen strange lights before a number of other earthquakes around the world, but the ones near Charnwood seem to be the first time such lights before an earthquake were noticed. Well, at least noticed and written down.'

'Oh you run deep, you do. Trust you to be a know it all about ev'rythin'.'

'Not really. Just that I read a few days ago about such lights before an earthquake in Japan in 1968 and more recently before the big Turkish one in 1999. And, here in Britain, there were weird lights before the Cornish earthquake of 10th November 1996. It all put me in mind of a couple of young chaps who came round some years ago asking loads of questions. That would have been back in the early 1970s.

They had a right curious way of thinking. They said they were trying to find out everything about what folk at the time called UFOs, which had become a bit of a craze in the 50s and 60s, because these lads thought these UFOs were really these lights created from the earth that were unknown to science.'

> 'Thought UFOs was spacecraft with little green men in them, come from other stars to check up on us.'

'What, and stop on someone's back lawn and have a nice cup of tea and a slice of cake before flitting off back to Beetlejuice? Give us a break! All sounds a bit potty to me. No, it seems these lads thought the whole idea of UFOs being evidence for extraterrestrials was a bit barking. And that was quite radical thinking, mind, at the time when they were doing their researches. One of them went on to write a book about it all, and all these questions they'd been asking in Leicestershire became a key part of it.'

> 'Oh, so it only 'appens in Leicestershire then.'

'No, you daft devil, just that they did the research round here.'

> 'My stars! What do yer mean? Yo're at it agen! Yo'd best not keep on calling me a daft bugga an' all else you'll come a cropper. It's a fine ol' doings when you're called so by someone you thought was a friend.'

'Now, be said... '

> 'I'll let yer know what's what, and in no uncertain terms, I will. You favour [take after] your mutha, yo' do. She were a nice article too – a right Tartar if ever there were, right down to the ground. She were alw'ys edging for a foight, and there's few as'ud [as would] stick up to 'er. Not a second time, anyways. There weren't a woman in the town who could swear like what that woman could!. In fact, I don't think

I've ever knowd a badder woman nor what that
woman were! She were the baddest of a pretty
difficult lot in your family, she were. There wern'
many as could abide any of the lot of 'em. And they
could neva 'it it off between 'emselves, neither.
They'd alw'ys differ so. Y'd be a bigger fool nor what
anyone thought yer to tek any notice of any ot 'em, if
you could avoid it ... '

'Hold your noise! Drop it now, can't you? I'm not getting
stroppy with you! For a start off, I can't do now't about me
motha, she's been dead going on fifty year. Never could
abide her much myself, truth be told. 'Tain't fair that
everyone says I take after her. I don't expect as many folk
did take a shine to her. Just 'cause she were a dab hand at
pocketing the odd bottle of gin and was always indulging
herself with the contents. There's plenty of other folk who,
in a manner of speaking, indulged themselves just as much as
what she did, so it ain't no crime. Not everyone wants to
drink Adam's Ale all the time.'

'Wot's Adam's Ale? Do yer mean Corporation Pop,
the stuff wot comes out the tap the kitchen?'

'Yes, that's the stuff – good old fashioned cold water.
Anyhow, can you eat another piece of cake?'

'I can that, thank you kindly. Oh no! Yer gin me too
much!

'Oh well, eat what you want and leave the rest. Anyways, as
I was saying, since the lad's book came out lots of other folk
have looked at these so-called UFOs and found the same thing
happening in parts of America and goodness knows where
else. There's a place in Norway where they seem to happen
nearly all the time, so there's lots of photos and such.'

'Wor'else did they come up wi'?'

'Oh loads of stuff. I don't think half of what they came up
with ended up in the books or anything. Seems that the

Charnwood Forest area experiences quite a lot of earthquakes. Not many of them are as big that folks would really notice, mind.'

'Well I can understand there being tremors up 'round Coalville or Desford, what with all the mining.'

'But it weren't where the mining was going on – Sapcote also experienced at least three earthquakes in the early 1970s. And the mines don't go under Charnwood Forest, or out to Sapcote, or such like. And in the eighteenth century, long before the big coal mines, there's reports of quite a few earthquakes around the county too. There was a big one at Shepshed on 18th July 1727. For some years before that, between 1715 and 1724, the vicar at Shepshed had been reporting strange 'aurorae'. Much later on there were strange rapidly flashing lights in the sky around Loughborough in August 1892.

'Truth be told, they were also reporting all sorts of strange noises from the sky too. Such noises were reported from around Hinckley in 1672 and again from over at Buckminster in the 1720s. Meteorites were happening from time to time too, as they tend to do. The most famous ones were seen – and most certainly heard – at Markfield in 1649. There was all sorts of flashes and bangs in the sky, then the written account makes out that what landed was dirty great chunks of ice, looking like axes and daggers. It was Hinckley's turn in the 1760s – a couple of meteorite storms there in October and December 1766 and another in October 1769.

'So it weren' just lightnin' and after claps of thunda then?'

'No, 'cause the parsons and such like who wrote about these things would have known all about thunder storms. You've got to remember that at that time scientists believed that meteorites couldn't came from outer space – they thought such an idea was superstitious nonsense – so they thought they were a type of strange weather phenomenon. Which is why the word 'meteorite' and the posh word for studying the weather, 'meteorology', start the same, even though scientists finally had to accept meteorites really were extra-terrestrial by 1805.'

'But that bleddeh big un wot 'it Barwell on Chris'mas Eve was certainly from outa space, wern' it?'

'It certainly was big – the biggest that's hit anywhere in this country since folk started taking an interest. That was back in 1965 and it's still the biggest so far – though it had broken up into lots of smaller pieces by the time they landed. That's probably just as well, as otherwise it might have done a lot more damage. There were lights in the sky alright before that lot came to earth – there were people for miles around, right out into Warwickshire and goodness knows where, who said they saw them.'

'Goin' back to what we was talkin' abart jus' now, and them stones. Wer'n' there one up near Bottesf'd that fell from the sky? Wer'n' it called the Star Stone or sumit [something] like?'

'You're right, thinking about it. It's not there now, but you can work out where it was 'cause it marked where the three counties of Leicestershire, Lincolnshire and Nottinghamshire come together.

'While we're thinking of stones again, I should have mentioned the one at Grimston, with the stocks right alongside it. Local lore says that it fell from the sky although it don't seem likely as it's not the right sort of rock. Some years ago folk there told of another stone, a bigger one, and that was also supposed to have fallen from the sky. Would have made a hole half the size of the village if it had of done! That stone got used to fill in a pond, so there's no way of telling what sort of rock it was made of.'

'But you just sed that not so long back people di'n' believe that stones – meteorites – kem [came] from outa space at all. So 'ow come there's all this folklore wot says they're fallen stars an' all?'

'Yes, it's a bit contrary, i'n'it? The answer may be that there's lots of Classical myths about thunderbolts and rocks that are said to be gifts from Zeus and the other Greek deities who were thought to be dashing around up in the heavens. So people may well have heard those tales, certainly by the eighteenth century, and adapted them to local landmarks. Then you've got to realise that the same sort of people at the end of the eighteenth century who were interested in whether or not meteorites were caused by the weather or were from beyond the sky itself were, by and large, the same sort of folk who were interested in Classical myths and in writing down folklore and such like. Now we'll never know to what extent they wrote down what they heard, or what they wanted to hear, or even made a few guesses... '

'You mean, med it up as they went along....'

'Well, perhaps not intentionally, just that they believed something to be true, so when they found some evidence to support their beliefs they wrote it down. Whereas they didn't write down anything which didn't support their original ideas. Just as folk generally only remember what they want to remember, eh? But once some folklore has been written down, it just keeps getting retold, and gets a little more garbled or elaborated as time goes by.'

'So wot you're saying is that we'll never know whether the folklore about these "Star Stones" and such like really does go back before the people who wrote down such legends? But i'n't that quite different to all this UFO stuff?

'Well, if scientists had to change their minds big time about meteorites, perhaps they need to about UFOs too. Least that's what them local lads were hoping. Hasn't really happened yet, though I don't think anyone's proved them wrong either. But if it weren't for all that folklore and such like that they came across by looking hard at old papers and records about Leicestershire, then they wouldn't have come up with the evidence they needed to support their ideas. And another part of their thinking was that these odd lights didn't just get called UFOs but that some of them stayed nearer the ground and people called them ghosts – especially the 'white lady' sort. Which is kinda neat because, as were saying the other night, there's loads of ghosts – including the White Lady one at the ruins of Grace Dieu Priory – all along the Loughborough to Ashby road, which is also the northern edge of Charnwood and there is a geological fault in the rocks more or less underneath for most of its length.'

> 'Ay've gorra friend ova at Whit'ick who walks her dog twice a day round in the woods near there – the ones near the edge of the quarry. She seys more than once she seen weird little lights when its dark. Calls them "earthlights".'

'Ah, that's what the lad's book's called – bet she's read it. And the edge of a big quarry would be just the sort of place where the rocks are stressed, so would fit with the theory. That's a bit more evidence to back it up, then.'

> 'So Ay'd better keep watching the skies then – but not because E.T.'s about to come round to my home, eh?'

'Go on with yer.'

> 'My aunt! Is that the time! I'd berra [better] be gerrin' off straightaway else the Old Man will be causing a runction about me gallivanting about when there's no end of work to do. I'm glad I catched yer. I'll come again as Wensdy, that's for sure. Anyway, same as Ay sed, Ay'd berra be gerrin' off. Ta Tah!'

'Ta-ra Ethel'

Whence living waters flow

Chapter 8

Whence living waters flow

Get's you thinking dun' it? It's only in the 1930s that most of the rural parts of Leicestershire got piped water, so until then everyone had relied on wells and pumps. There must have been a heck of a lot of them. Yet by the 1980s no one knew much about any of them – they'd been capped over, filled in or whatever. Just fifty years, less than a lifetime, and something so necessary and commonplace was all but quite forgotten. Makes you wonder about everything else that just disappears without any memories.

Though not everything has been forgotten. Some of the best folklore from round these parts is about wells, and how they were discovered – usually a bit weird and wonderful. Not like X Files but more in line with medieval notions of miracles, which I suppose were the next best think to sci-fi in their day.

One of my favourite accounts of finding a well involves two sisters who were living at the little village of Hoton, past Loughborough, sometime soon after 1500. There had been a drought for the last three or four months that was causing serious problems for the villagers. The sisters' father was a farmer and, like all the other farmers there, his livestock were suffering badly from lack of water. They risked many of the animals dying and loosing a great deal of money as a result. One of the sisters, Gertrude Lacy, woke up one night after a strange dream. All excited, she went over to her sister and woke her and says to her how, in the dream, she had taken a pilgrim's staff that had been all the way to the Holy Land and back, and gone over between Hoton and Wymeswold to a place she recognised as Langdale field. She'd then thrust the staff into the ground, and a stream of fresh water flowed out.

Her sister, Grace, wasn't anything like as excited about being woken in the middle of the night and having her sister gabble away telling her this nutty dream. "You should realise that dreams are no but dreams, and ain't like what real life is," she rebuked her over-excited sister.

Anyway, the next night Gertrude had exactly the same dream. Grace was still rather sceptical about it all, and said 'Where do you think you're going to get pilgrim's staff from?', to which Gertrude could only say she didn't know. However for three night's running Gertrude had the same dream, and after the third time she thought that by now other people should know, not just Grace. All along of Gertrude being so enthusiastic, or perhaps because they were getting desperate for water and would have tried anything, the villagers decided they should give it a go. And then one of the men said he knew where a staff that had been brought back from Canaan had been buried. So the man what knew about the staff went and dug it up. Gertrude grabbed hold of it and carried it over to Langdale field. Grace walked beside her and all the villagers went along behind them. After a brief prayer, she plunged the staff into the ground in the place she had seen in her dream. Lo and behold, clear water started bubbling out. "We done it!" she shouted. Soon the water was going great guns and within a few minutes a stream had started to flow.

The villagers were dead chuffed – here was the answer to all their problems! A stone surround was built and the well was known as the Sisters' Well, or the Two Sisters' Well, although later on some took to referring to it as Jacob's Well, after the Biblical story. When the RAF built an airfield there in the 1940s the well was capped over with concrete, though the water's probably still flowing underneath if anyone was able to see.

Interestingly, there's an unusual double effigy over at nearby Prestwold church that depicts two ladies. They're quite plainly dressed, and both dressed almost the same, apart from slightly different jewellery. To them that knows about such things, the slightly pointed headdresses and the style of their dresses suggest that the ladies lived around 1500, give or take a couple of decades as fashions didn't change as fast then as they do now. They certainly look like two sisters and the locals say they're the same sisters who discovered the well. The date seems about right, that's for sure.

The locals also say they're the same sisters who built the bridge over the Trent at Swarkestone after their lovers were drowned trying to get across, and who might have something to do with the building of the similar bridge over the Soar at Cotes, which is just down from Hoton and Prestwold. However these bridges date from the thirteenth century, as does the legend about the drowned lovers – who are said to have been knights serving Simon de Montfort in his battle against King Henry III in 1265. So whoever the sisters were that might have got involved in one or other bridges, it seems they'd have been dead the best part of two hundred years before the effigy at Prestwold was carved, so it seems more than a tad unlikely that the effigy has anything to do with them. You shouldn't believe everything the books on folklore say, eh?

Another well where a young lady features large in the legend has just come to mind, though the circumstance are quite different. The young lady's name was Elizabeth Ferrers and she was the daughter of Lord Ferrers of Groby. According to all accounts, not only were the family well-off but she was drop-dead gorgeous an' all. She was promised in marriage – as they used to say – to Sir Edward Grey, an ancestor of Lady Jane Grey.

Well, none the less she caught the attention of Lord Comyn who lived at Whitwick. He was a big chap, very strong but not so well equipped with good manners. He was certainly not given to romantic love or to winning his women over with words – when Lady Elizabeth refused his advances he simply told some of his men to kidnap her and bring her to him.

Comyn's men had to bide their time for a while, because Elizabeth had got wind of this and was rather wary. But one day she went off riding with just a few friends, and Comyn's henchmen knew they had a chance. So they overpowered those who were with her. But not before they had distracted Comyn's men long enough for Elizabeth to sneak away and give them the slip. When the men reported what had happened to Lord Comyn he blew his top, and told them they had to go back and scour Charnwood Forest till they found her.

Trouble was that the weather had turned for the worse, so they got wet through with the rain, and the wind made them cold. But things were even worse for Elizabeth, as she wasn't dressed for the bad weather and was struggling to find her way as it got dark. She'd made it as far as the rocks above Woodhouse Eaves and headed towards the Outwoods. When she could hear Comyn's men in the distance she hid inside a hollow oak tree till they'd gone past.

But her troubles weren't over because now the weather turned really foul, with thunder and lightning. However, she knew there was a little hermitage protected by a moat just past the edge of the woods, so she set off in that direction. Before making herself known to the monks who lived there she went round to the side where they was a holy well to take a much-needed drink. But the exertion of her journey and the effects of the cold and wet had taken their toll on her, and she passed out before she got to the water.

At first light one of the monks got up to go to where he prayed each morning. Just a few steps away from the hermitage he found Elizabeth's body. She looked so pale he assumed she was dead. But he lifted her up and began praying and, using a scallop shell that he had taken on pilgrimage all the way to Santiago de Compostella and back, he sprinkled the holy water on her face. I suppose he was chuntering away to her in Latin – though for all I know he could just been saying that 'This'll do you the power of good, m'duck'! Anyway, within a minute or so she'd recovered her senses and, though the ordeal had made her proper poorly, she went on to make a full recovery.

Soon after, in 1446, Lady Elizabeth married her rightful suitor at Ulverscroft Priory. They both went back to the monks at the hermitage and thanked them by making a gift of some land plus a promise of three deer a year. The hermitage still stands. Or at least parts of it, such as the doorway, are incorporated into the farmhouse, which is now known as Holywell Hall. Only that's a bit of a cock up as it was known for a long time as Holywell Haw – the word 'haw' means an enclosure, in the same way that 'hawthorn' is the thorn bush used for making hedges and other enclosures, though in this case the 'haw' probably referred to the moat rather than a hedge.

The holy well is still there, though it doesn't look very holy as it's a very practical concrete construction. The water still flows really well and the farmer relied on it for many years. The moat was filled in a long time ago, but otherwise it's much as it was – if you can ignore the massive British Gas research place just the other side of the trees.

With this being folklore and all that, you shouldn't believe everything you read. Certainly there's more than a bit of problem with one of the better-known versions of this tale, which makes out it was Agnes Litherland, not Elizabeth Ferrers, who was the young lady. But Agnes Litherland lived nearly a hundred years later and her claim to fame was being the prioress in charge of Grace Dieu at the time of the Dissolution. The confusion might arise because she tried to escape Henry VIII's men – perhaps running off with some of the valuables – but doesn't seem to have succeeded. There's also a complicated tale about how when she was young she escaped from an unpleasant husband she 'acquired' while over in Cadiz, but I'll save that tale for another time.

For that matter there's loads of other holy wells in Leicestershire that I could tell you about, but if any of them ever had any interesting legends then they've not come down to us.

Springtime customs

Chapter 9

Springtime customs

Tomorrow's Easter Monday, so if the weather's as good as it is today I fancy popping over to Hallaton for a bit of hare pie scrambling and bottle kicking. Best to go over every few years to see how the old tradition is being kept up – and keep an eye on the changes that creep in.

I remember when that chap – nice kind of gent he was – was going round collecting folklore and such like. It's a while ago now, must have been when Victoria was still on the throne. What was his name? Something like Charles Wilson... No that can't be right... Never was much good with names, and it was quite a while back. Might come to me later. Anyway he ends up writing a neat little account of the goings on at Hallaton at the time:

> On Easter Monday in every year a procession is formed in the following order:
>
> Two men abreast, carrying sacks full of hare pies.
>
> Three men abreast, carrying aloft a bottle each, two of which are filled with beer and the third is a wooden dummy.
>
> A hare (if it can be procured) in a sitting posture, mounted on top of a pole.
>
> The procession was also formerly accompanied by a man carrying a sack full of bread, which he threw out to be caught by the company.

This little troop, followed by the townspeople and a band of music, marches to an ancient earthwork about a quarter of a mile south of the town, consisting of a small oblong bank with a narrow trench round it and a circular hole in the centre. This is known as 'Hare-pie Bank'. The pies are here tumbled out of the sacks and scrambled for by the crowd. Then begins the well-known 'Hallaton Bottle-Kicking'. The bottles containing the beer are first thrown into the circular hollow, and then the dummy bottle, for which all scramble, and the men of Medbourne or other villagers try to wrest it from the Hallatonians' grasp, and try to force it over the brook which forms the parish boundary.

Nobody wrote anything about either the Hare Pie Scramble or the Bottle Kicking before the eighteenth century. Maybe they started as two separate events on two different days – the Bottle Kicking is rather akin to the street football that used to take place in many towns on Shrove Tuesday but now only survives at Atherstone, just over the border in Warwickshire, Ashbourne up in Derbyshire, and at a few other far-flung places such as Corfe Castle. For that matter there's the Haxey Hood Game in Lincolnshire, but that's on Old Midwinter's Day, which always falls on 6th January.

Leicester didn't have street football as such, at least so far as we know, but there was a street version of hockey, referred to variously as shinney, or shindy or shinty. If you've ever played hockey you'll know darned well that the shins can get a far old bashing from the other side's sticks – and not always purely accidentally – so I think we can guess where the 'shinney' bit comes from. In fact there were several rowdy customs at Shrovetide, all taking place in The Newarke. One was throwing sticks at cocks – you paid to throw six sticks at the poor bird and, if you killed it, it was yours to keep. That delightful 'sport' was abolished in 1784. But the shinney and the Whipping Toms continued until 1846. Originally the

Whipping Toms were there to clear the streets after the shinney game but in the end they became part of the days' fun too. Just before it was abolished someone wrote this account:

> So soon as the Pancake Bell rang, men and boys assembled with sticks having a knob or hook at the end. A wooden ball was thrown down, and two parties engaged in striving which could get the ball, by stricking it with their sticks, to one end of the Newarke first – those who did so were the victors. The game was called 'Hockey' or 'Shinney'. About one o'clock the Whipping Toms appeared on the scene of action. These were men clad in blue smock frocks, with long waggon whips, who were accompanied by three men with small bells. They commenced driving the men and boys out of the Newarke. It was very danagerous sometimes; and they would lash the whip in such a manner round the legs of those they were pursuing as to throw them down, which produced laughter and shouting. Some would stop, and turn to the whipper and say, 'Let's have a pennyworth,' and he would guard and parry off the blows with his shinney stick. When the whipper was successful in lashing him, he demanded his penny, and continued his lashing until he paid. This was continued until five o'clock, then the game terminated.

All good fun, eh? Other writers give us a bit more detail. Seems that the Whipping Toms were not allowed to whip anyone above the knee, nor whip anyone who was kneeling, nor outside certain boundaries, or if they paid a small fine. However clearly lots of chaps thought it was good fun to run the gauntlet of the Toms, rather as if they were Spaniards running before bulls. Sensibly they wore knee-length boots and had their shinney sticks to parry the whip lashes. Predictably enough the local gentry were not at all keen on the common folk having such fun, so they made various attempts to stop it. None of them were successful until an

Act of Parliament was passed in 1846 that tried to put paid to the goings on. The fine for anyone caught taking part at 'Whipping Toms, shindy, football, or any other game' was set at five pounds – a huge amount in those days. Despite this the next year a huge crowd gathered, which was matched by a large number of police and a full riot developed. But that was the last of the Shrovetide sports in Leicester.

Quite possibly at around that time there was a serious attempt to suppress the bottle kicking at Hallaton – which may well have taken place in the streets of the village originally – so the lads who wanted to keep up that custom just 'hijacked' the Easter Monday hare pie malarkey. After all Easter Monday was the day for another hare-related custom in Leicestershire, when there was a ritual hare hunt out at my neck of the woods at the Dane Hills. That stopped quite a while ago, mind, certainly by the later part of the eighteenth century. And even then they'd stopped trying to find hares and substituted a dead cat soaked in aniseed. Nevertheless they made a right to do of it and the huntsman and hounds rode at full cry through to Leicester and ended up at the mayor's door, where he was 'obliged' to provide food and drink. Some say that a similar custom also took place at Whetstone.

In the later part of the nineteenth century British folklorists became a bit obsessed with the idea that folk customs were like 'fossils' of pre-Christian pagan customs. There was a suggestion that Easter got its name from an otherwise unknown pagan goddess called Eostre, whose sacred animal was the hare. The origin of this idea is dead dodgy, but none the less it's been accepted as true by loads of folk. Other folklore says that hares were witches' familiars, or that witches could shape-shift into hares. So, Bingo!, both Easter bunnies and the hare pie scramble all have to be pagan survivals. Actually it's all a load of cobblers. Academics interested in pagan goddesses don't take the notion of a goddess called Eostre at all seriously. And, as for the stuff about 'pagan survivals', this has been well and truly sorted out by the more serious sort of folklorists during the last thirty-or-so years. They have shown how it was all invented from some dubious eighteenth century Christian propaganda, then took hold among folklorists a bit too keen on finding a Grand Theory of Everything in the nineteenth century.

Reality is that very few folk customs survived the seventeenth century as the Puritans suppressed all merrymaking for at least thirty years. Those customs that restarted when Charles II was restored to the throne were usually more than a little bit different to what had gone before. However in the nature of these things, the goings on at Hallaton are now widely thought of as being a continuation of a pagan custom and this nonsense has been kept alive in recent books by folk that really out to have done just a little bit of homework. Or maybe they just think that fragments of fanciful fiction are better than a few facts.

All we really know of the origins of the Hallaton activities is that someone left the rector a piece of land called Hare Pie Leys on the condition that every Easter he provided two hare pies, some ale and two dozen penny loaves. The custom gets amended in 1770 when, because of the Enclosure Award, Hare Pie Bank is substituted for the original land. We also know for certain that there were attempts to stop the custom. In 1790 the rector of Hallaton decided he didn't want to supply the hare pie and thought the money could be used in better ways. But on the walls of the rectory and the church he found chalked the slogan "No pie, no parson and a job for the glazier." He took the hint. Indeed the only time the custom has not taken place was in 2001 as a result of the foot and mouth crisis. At that time it emerged that the custom had been kept up during the World Wars, although the women took part in the boisterous bottle kicking as the men were away fighting. Shame no one thought to take a photo or two back then!

The event that takes place now starts with a couple of processions. The first of them starts from the pub, usually the Fox, and is headed up by a band. Then comes two women holding the big hare pie between them. Yes, it does contain hare meat – and lots of vegetables – even though Easter is closed season for hare hunting. Where would traditional customs be without them new-fangled deep-freezers, eh? Behind them are three hefty-looking lads, holding up the bottles above their heads with one arm. Well they're small wooden casks about a foot high, but 'bottles' is what farm labourers used to call them when they kept their daily ration of ale in them. Two of the bottles contain beer and one is a dummy; this is the one that will be 'kicked' –though it's broken toes for anyone daft enough to try giving it the boot.

Behind them is the crowd of villagers and visitors, several hundred of them. Makes a right impressive sight. They go as far as the churchyard gate where the rector is waiting for them. He blesses the pie – although some years it's just three cheers for the pie depending on how uptight the clergyman is – and then he starts to neatly slice it. Bit of a waste of time that as everyone crowds in and tries to get a handful. Most of it is chucked out into the crowd – dead easy to get an eyeful without trying. Just a bit of the pie is kept back and put in a sack for later on.

Everyone then moves over to what they know as the "cross", though it looks like a big stone cone with a little ball perched on – what looks like a cross is known as the war memorial. The rector then ties coloured ribbons around the bottles and, in recent years, bread rolls are chucked out the crowd.

Then everyone goes back to the pub for an hour or two. For those taking part in the bottle kicking this is fairly essential preparation. The bottles hold nine pints of beer and, as many wags have suggested, this is about how much beer the participants need to have inside them too before even contemplating taking part in the bottle kicking. Prodigious beer consumption is an essential part of team tactics. Not only would no sober person enter such an affray but, to some extent, the alcohol has a medicinal effect in deadening the inevitable pain. Anyway, time comes for another procession. Not for nothing did one of the bottle bearers take up his position in the parade one year with the words "This is where the beer does the talking."

This time the three lads line up, holding the bottles aloft. Everyone goes past the church this time and along the road up the hill out of the village to the top of a steep field. When they get there the rest of the hare pie is tossed to the crowd. Then the dummy bottle is thrown in the air three times. The last time it comes down it's 'Game on!' and upwards of fifty lads form a scrum that makes rugby look decidedly like a game for the limp-wristed. At some point the bottle breaks free and, at least for a moment, the players moved fast, threatening to engulf nearby spectators. But the scrum quickly reforms, leaving the lads who had been underneath the former scrum to get their breath back.

The aim is for the Hallatonians to get the bottle to the bottom of the hill and across the brook, or for the lads from the nearby village of Melbourne (in practice anyone who is not from Hallaton plays for the 'away' team) to get the bottle across several hedge and a ditch much further away. What do you mean "That ain't fair?" Who said games had to be fair?

Anyway it's the best of three games. The first game is always the longest – it often takes a couple of hours. Of course, if the score gets to 2–0 then there's no third game. So then its off back to the village green, where the captain of the victorious team takes a drink from one of the 'real' bottles and then shares the rest with his team, and – as it was all for fun really – with the opposition.

However, as with other traditional customs, nothing remains static. In 1994 the 'hare on a pole' mentioned in the 1890s was reintroduced – but in the form of a half-life-size bronze sculpture, produced by a sculptor who lived in Hallaton. And he's shown the hare leaping rather than sitting on top of the pole. Although inflation had caught up with the penny loaves by 1982 – by then even a small cob cost more than a penny, a new penny at that, so the bread was forgotten about

– at the same time as the hare sculpture appeared the basket of bread rolls reappeared too.

The people carrying the hare and the basket of bread rolls may have tried hard to bring back part of the tradition but they quite broke with tradition by appearing in 'fancy dress' costume. They're dressed up to the nines in finery of an indeterminate 'oldness' which looks dead odd when all the other participants are dressed in old clothes suitable for the rough-and-tumble of the bottle kicking. Indeed there was a time when anyone who appeared in the procession looking a bit too 'posh' – such as wearing a top hat – would have got mud slung at them. Perhaps that's part of the tradition that should be brought back too, eh? Even more recently the key players from the Medbourne side have appeared wearing 'team colours' – rugby shirts with some interestingly rude nicknames on the back. As they say, everything always changes, and that's certainly true of 'traditions'.

Final words

There's no end of oddments of tales and traditions from hereabouts I could have told you about. But they'll have to wait till I feel in the mood again. Hope you think as this lot been better than a poke in the eye with a burnt stick.

What do you mean 'No!"? You'll gerrit when I catch you, you little tike! You'll gerra good hidin', you will! That'll give yer summat to blurt about! You'll know on it when I cop 'old of you...

Acknowledgements

I am of course especially grateful to all those who have helped to keep Leicestershire legends alive by previously writing and publishing various retellings. However, some chapters of this book include research which has not previously appeared in collections of local lore. In particular, several sections draw extensively on the research of Andrew York which he prepared in collaboration with Paul Devereux during the 1970s; Paul kindly provided copies of their more obscure articles (see 'Sources' on the following pages) and loaned Andrews' letters and notes. My most grateful thanks to them both.

Access to many of the older retellings of Leicestershire legends was made possible because of the availability of relevant books from Leicestershire Libraries; my thanks to the staff for the extensive assistance they have provided during nineteen years of research into Leicestershire legends, local history, and much else. Aubrey Stevenson at the Record Office for Leicestershire, Leicester and Rutland kindly provided prompt assistance with specific bibliographical details. Cynthia Brown, while she was running the East Midlands Oral History Archive, most helpfully made me aware of local dialect researchers.

Sarah Allen, Jenny Clarke, Clifford Dunkley, Rhianydd Murray and others kindly read all or part of either an earlier draft or the page proofs. Enthusiastic feedback from those who read the draft version in whole or part greatly encouraged the preparation of the revised version. The way Jenny interpreted the brief for the illustrations greatly exceeded expectations and adds greatly to the appeal of this book. Special thanks to Clifford for making extensive comments on the way dialect is incorporated into these stories (although he may not necessarily agree with my final attempts) and for allowing the 'Guide to Leicester dialect' section to be based on parts of his booklet *Let's Talk Leicester*.

Eclectic projects such as this are built up from numerous small, seemingly incidental, snippets of information so my thanks to everyone else who has helped over the years, directly or indirectly – no matter how small they consider their contribution.

SOURCES

Introduction

David Bell, *Leicestershire and Rutland Ghosts and Legends,* Countryside Books, 1992, p29–31.

Charles Billson, 'Vestiges of Paganism in Leicestershire', in Alice Dryden (ed), *Memorials of Old Leicestershire Vestiges of Paganism in Leicestershire,* George Allen, 1911; reprinted as *Vestiges of Paganism in Leicestershire,* Heart of Albion Press, 1985, p7–8.

Susan E. Green, *Selected Legends of Leicestershire,* Leicester Research Services, 1971, p28–9.

John Heyrick, 'On a cave called Black Annis's Bower', *First Flights,* 1797.

Ronald Hutton, *The Triumph of the Moon,* Oxford UP, 1999, p274–5.

Roy Palmer, *Folklore of Leicestershire and Rutland* (2nd edn), Tempus, 2002, p29–30.

Eric Swift, *Folk Tales of the East Midlands,* Nelson, 1954, p90.

Chapter 1

David Bell, *Leicestershire and Rutland Ghosts and Legends,* Countryside Books, 1992, p10–11; p49–51.

Charles Billson, 'Vestiges of Paganism in Leicestershire', in Alice Dryden (ed), *Memorials of Old Leicestershire Vestiges of Paganism in Leicestershire,* George Allen, 1911; reprinted as *Vestiges of Paganism in Leicestershire,* Heart of Albion Press, 1985, p6–7.

Jill Bourne, *Understanding Leicestershire and Rutland Place-names,* Heart of Albion Press, 2003, p58–9.

Mike Dixon-Kennedy, *Celtic Myth and Legend,* Blandford,1996.

Marian Pipe, *Tales of Old Leicestershire,* Countryside Books, 1991; 2nd edn 1999, p108–10.

Sources

Chapter 2

David Bell, *Leicestershire and Rutland Ghosts and Legends,* Countryside Books, 1992, p11–13, p32–3.

Charles Billson, 'Vestiges of Paganism in Leicestershire', in Alice Dryden (ed), *Memorials of Old Leicestershire Vestiges of Paganism in Leicestershire,* George Allen, 1911; reprinted as *Vestiges of Paganism in Leicestershire,* Heart of Albion Press, 1985, p10–11.

D.J. Bott, 'The murder of St Wistan', *Transactions of the Leicestershire Archaeological and Historical Society,* Vol. 29, 1953.

Susan Green, *Selected Legends of Leicestershire and Rutland,* Leicester Research Services, 1971, p18–19, p32–9.

'Heywood', *Local Legends,* Echo Press 1934, p59–62.

Roy Palmer, *Folklore of Leicestershire and Rutland* (2nd edn), Tempus, 2002, p239–47.

Marian Pipe, *Tales of Old Leicestershire,* Countryside Books, 1991; 2nd edn 1999 p104–7, p111–15.

Pruett, John H., 1978–9, 'A late Stuart Leicestershire parson: the Reverend Humphrey Michel', *Transactions of the Leicestershire Archaeological and Historical Society* Vol.54, p26–38.

Chapter 3

Charles Billson, 'Vestiges of Paganism in Leicestershire', in Alice Dryden (ed), *Memorials of Old Leicestershire Vestiges of Paganism in Leicestershire,* George Allen, 1911; reprinted as *Vestiges of Paganism in Leicestershire,* Heart of Albion Press, 1985, p10–11.

D.J. Bott, 'The murder of St Wistan', *Transactions of the Leicestershire Archaeological and Historical Society,* Vol. 29, 1953.

Susan Green, *Selected Legends of Leicestershire and Rutland,* Leicester Research Services, 1971, p5–7.

Malcolm Jones, *The Secret Middle Ages: Discovering the real medieval world,* Sutton Publishing, 2002, p154.

Roy Palmer, *Folklore of Leicestershire and Rutland* (2nd edn), Tempus, 2002, p28; p37.

C.I. Williams, letter regarding Hathern Piper's Hole, *Leicester Mercury,* 29th October 1971.

Chapter 4

David Bell, *Leicestershire and Rutland Ghosts and Legends,*
Countryside Books, 1992, p84–5; p89–91; p105–6.
Gillian Bennett, *Alas Poor Ghost! Traditions of belief in story and
discourse,* Utah State University Press, 1999.
Angela Cutting, *Leicestershire Ghost Stories,* Anderson Publications
1982, p15; p28.
Susan Green, *Further Legends of Leicestershire and Rutland,*
Chamberlain Music and Books, 1985, p16–18.
Mr and Mrs Griffiths, lecture to Wolds Historical Organisation 16th
February 1993 about Loughborough to Ashby road.
Elliott O'Donnell, *Haunted Churches,* Quality Press, 1939, p61
Jeremy Harte, 'Cavaliers and phantoms', *3rd Stone,* No.26 (Summer
1997), p6–10.
Roy Palmer, *Folklore of Leicestershire and Rutland* (2nd edn),
Tempus, 2002, p227.
Janet Slattery, 'Grace Dieu's ghost', *The Lady,* 23rd Jan 1990.

All the following were brought to my attention by the research of
Andrew York, kindly made available by Paul Devereux:

Coalville Times 3rd June 1966 (ghost at Drum and Monkey,
Thringstone)
Leicester Mercury 20th September 1968 (ghost of old lady in red
coat)
Leicester Mercury 17th June 1972 (ghost at Freewheeler Club,
Churchgate)
Leicester Mercury 23rd June 1972 (ghost at the Woodmans Stroke,
Rothley)
Leicester Mercury 22nd January 1973 (exorcism of Britella factory,
Frog Island)

Chapter 5

David Bell, *Leicestershire and Rutland Ghosts and Legends,*
Countryside Books, 1992, p5–6.
Paul Devereux and Andrew York, 'Portrait of a fault area, Part 2' in
The News, (now *Fortean Times*), No.12, 1975.
John Nichols, *History and Antiquities of the County of Leicester,*
1795–1815.

Sources

Roy Palmer, *Folklore of Leicestershire and Rutland* (2nd edn),
Tempus, 2002, p221.

Paul Sieveking, 'Millennium moggy survey', *Fortean Times*, No.146,
(2001) p16–17. (Alien big cats)

Eric Swift, *Folk Tales of the East Midlands*, Nelson, 1954.

Bob Trubshaw (ed), *Explore Phantom Black Dogs*, Heart of Albion
(forthcoming 2005).

Chapter 6

David Bell, *Leicestershire and Rutland Ghosts and Legends*,
Countryside Books 1992, p67–7; p91–3.

Charles Billson, 'Vestiges of Paganism in Leicestershire', in Alice
Dryden (ed), *Memorials of Old Leicestershire Vestiges of
Paganism in Leicestershire*, George Allen, 1911; reprinted as
Vestiges of Paganism in Leicestershire, Heart of Albion Press,
1985, p12–16.

M.P. Dare, *Charnwood Forest*, Backus, 1925.

Jeremy Harte, 'The power of lonely places', *Mercian Mysteries*,
No.23, 1995, 8–13; online at
www.indigogroup.co.uk/edge/crockern.htm

'Heywood', *Local Legends*, Echo Press 1934, p27–31.

William Kelly, *Royal Progress and Visits to Leicestershire*, 1815.

Paul Devereux, 'The forgotten heart of Albion, Part 1' in *The Ley
Hunter*, No. 67, 1975.

Paul Devereux and Andrew York, 'Portrait of a fault area, Part 2' in
The News, (now *Fortean Times*), No.12, 1975.

Susan Green, *Further Legends of Leicestershire and Rutland*,
Chamberlain Music and Books, 1985, p24–7.

T.R. Potter, *The History and Antiquities of Charnwood Forest*,
Hamilton Adams, 1842.

Bob Trubshaw, *Interactive Little-known Leicestershire and Rutland*,
Heart of Albion Press, 2002.

John Harold Worley, *Asfordby 1905–1922: Memories of a
Leicestershire village*, Heart of Albion Press, 1993.

Leicester Mercury 20th October 1990 (letter about the Wishing
Stone in Bradgate Park)

Leicester Mercury 31 July 1992 (Anstey standing stone and threat
from western bypass)

Chapter 7

Anon. *Fortean Times* No.96 (1997), p47 (anomalous lights before Cornish earthquake 10th November 1996).

Paul Devereux, *Earth Lights*, Turnstone 1982.

Paul Devereux, 'Welcome to the pisky party', *Fortean Times* No.96 (March 1997), p47 (anomalous lights preceding earthquake in Cornwall 10th November 1996).

Paul Devereux and Andrew York, 'Portrait of a fault area, Part 1' in *The News*, (now *Fortean Times*), No.11, 1975.

Paul Devereux and Andrew York, 'Portrait of a fault area, Part 2' in *The News*, (now *Fortean Times*), No.12, 1975.

Mike Jay, 'Cosmic Debris', *Fortean Times*, No. 143, February 2001.

Andy Roberts and David Clarke, 'Remember earthlights?', *Fortean Times*, No.178 (December 2003), p24 (US weather satellites show infrared anomalies ahead of earthquakes; earthlights preceded major 1999 earthquake in Turkey, and 1968 in Japan).

Personal correspondence from Andy York to Paul Devereux written in the early 1970s, kindly made available by Paul Devereux.

Chapter 8

David Bell, *Leicestershire and Rutland Ghosts and Legends*, Countryside Books 1992, p44–5.

Susan E. Green, *Selected Legends of Leicestershire*, Leicester Research Services, 1971, p20–3.

Susan Green, *Further Legends of Leicestershire and Rutland*, Chamberlain Music and Books, 1985, p5–7; p23.

'Heywood', *Local Legends*, Echo Press 1934, p7–11; p22–6; p32–7.

Roy Palmer, *Folklore of Leicestershire and Rutland* (2nd edn), Tempus, 2002, p32–3; p35–6.

Marian Pipe, *Tales of Old Leicestershire*, Countryside Books, 1991; 2nd edn 1999, p45–9.

Bob Trubshaw, *Interactive Little-known Leicestershire and Rutland*, Heart of Albion Press, 2002.

Philip White, 'The two unknown ladies of Prestwold', *Wolds Historical Organisation Newsletter*, 2001, p2–5.

Sarah Zaluckyj, *Mercia: The Anglo-Saxon kingdom of central England*, Logaston Press, 2001.

Sources

Chapter 9

Charles Billson, *County Folklore Leicestershire and Rutland*, Folklore Society, 1895.

Charles Billson, 'Vestiges of Paganism in Leicestershire', in Alice Dryden (ed), *Memorials of Old Leicestershire Vestiges of Paganism in Leicestershire*, George Allen, 1911; reprinted as *Vestiges of Paganism in Leicestershire*, Heart of Albion Press, 1985, p8–10; p17.

John Morison and Peter Daisley, *Hallaton Hare Pie Scambling and Bottle Kicking: Facts and Folklore of an Ancient Tradition*, Hallaton Museum, 2000.

Roy Palmer, *Folklore of Leicestershire and Rutland* (2nd edn), Tempus, 2002, p254.

Marian Pipe, *Tales of Old Leicestershire*, Countryside Books, 1991; 2nd edn 1999, p11–15.

Bob Trubshaw, *Interactive Little-known Leicestershire and Rutland*, Heart of Albion Press, 2002.

Bob Trubshaw, *Explore Folklore*, Heart of Albion Press, 2003, p37–41.

Dialect

Clifford Dunkley, *Let's Talk Leicester*, published by author, 1998.

Arthur B. Evans, *Leicestershire Words, Phrases and Proverbs*, T.C. Browne, 1848.

Roy Palmer, *Folklore of Leicestershire and Rutland*, Sycamore Press 1985; second edition Tempus 2002.

Richard Scollins and John Titford *Ey Up Mi Duck!: Dialect of Derbyshire and the East Midlands*, Countryside Books, 2000.

Peter Trudgill *The Dialects of England*, Basil Blackwell, 1990.

Clive Upton, Stewart Sanderson and John Widdowson, *Word Maps: A dialect atlas of England*, Croom Helm, 1987.

Rutland Village by Village

Bob Trubshaw

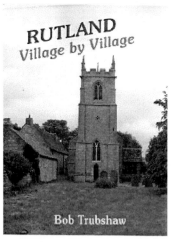

A guide to the history of all the villages in Rutland, with the emphasis on places that can be seen or visited. Based on the author's sixteen years of research into the little-known aspects of the county.

ISBN 1 872883 69 9. 2003, perfect bound. demi 8vo (215 x 138 mm), 73 + x pages, 53 b&w photos. **£6.95**

Little-Known Leicestershire and Rutland

Bob Trubshaw

Drawing upon nearly ten years of research into the holy wells, standing stones, medieval carvings and crosses of the county, this book gives 12 circular bicycle or car routes around unspoiled countryside. Introductory chapters are provided for those less familiar with these topics.

ISBN 1 872 883 40 0. 1995, A5, perfect bound, 128 pages, 9 photos, 14 maps, 49 drawings. **£6.95**

Understanding Leicestershire and Rutland Place-Names

Jill Bourne

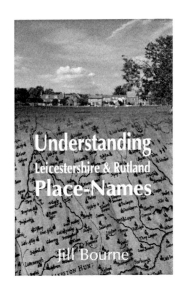

We take for granted the names we use for places. Yet these names are a valuable part of our cultural heritage, providing a detailed insight into the early history of the region. Place-names reveal the otherwise lost voices of our forebears who settled here.

Understanding Leicestershire and Rutland Place-Names analyses the whole range of place-names which occur in Leicestershire and Rutland, most of which were coined between 1,000 and 1,500 years ago. These place-names describe, often in fine detail, the landscape, geology, rivers, buildings, flora, fauna, boundaries, meeting places, roads and track-ways. This book also looks at the distribution of the names, the languages from which they are derived, the successive waves of conquerors and migrants who fought and settled here, and the society they created.

Jill Bourne is an historian, archaeologist and museum professional who has specialised in the area of place-name studies and landscape history for over 20 years.

ISBN 1872883 71 0. 2003, perfect bound. Demi 8vo (215 x 138 mm), 145 + viii pages, 5 maps. **£6.95**

Interactive Little-known Leicestershire and Rutland

Text and photographs by Bob Trubshaw

For seventeen years the author has been researching the 'little-known' aspects of Leicestershire and Rutland. Topics include holy wells, standing stones and mark stones, medieval crosses, and a wide variety of Romanesque and medieval figurative carvings - and a healthy quota of 'miscellaneous' sites.

Some of this information appeared in early Heart of Albion publications (mostly long out of print), but this CD-ROM contains extensive further research. The information covers 241 parishes and includes no less than 550 'large format' colour photographs (all previously unpublished).

There are introductory essays, a glossary and plenty of hypertext indexes.

Runs on PCs and Macs.

ISBN 1 872883 53 2. **£14.95** incl. VAT.

Special offer!

Mail order customers save 17.5% (because Heart of Albion is not VAT registered) = **£12.70**

Interactive Gargoyles and Grotesque Carvings of Leicestershire and Rutland

Text and photographs by Bob Trubshaw

A selection of images from *Interactive Little-known Leicestershire and Rutland* for those particularly interested in Romanesque and medieval figurative carvings. No less than 240 photos – including plenty of Green Men, tongue-pokers and a wide variety of other grotesques. Introductory text, glossary and plenty of hypertext indexes.

Runs on PCs and Macs.

ISBN 1 872883 57 5 **£11.75** incl. VAT.

Special offer! Because Heart of Albion is not VAT registered mail order customers save 17.5 percent = **£10.00**

Also published by Heart of Albion Press

Sepulchral Effigies in Leicestershire and Rutland

Text by Max Wade Matthews

Photographs by
Bob Trubshaw

This CD-ROM makes available for the first time details of the wealth of sepulchral effigies in Leicestershire and Rutland - from thirteenth century priests, thorough alabaster knights in armour and their ladies, to the splendours of seventeenth century Classical aggrandisement. There are even a number of twentieth century effigies too.
350 photos depict 141 effigies in 72 churches, all with detailed descriptions and useful hypertext indexes. Runs on PCs and Macs.

ISBN 1 872883 54 0 **£14.95** incl. VAT.

Special offer!

Mail order customers save 17.5% (because Heart of Albion is not VAT registered) = **£12.70**

Explore Fairy Traditions

Jeremy Harte

We are not alone. In the shadows of our countryside there lives a fairy race, older than humans, and not necessarily friendly to them. For hundreds of years, men and women have told stories about the strange people, beautiful as starlight, fierce as wolves, and heartless as ice. These are not tales for children. They reveal the fairies as a passionate, proud, brutal people.

Explore Fairy Traditions draws on legends, ballads and testimony from throughout Britain and Ireland to reveal what the fairies were really like. It looks at changelings, brownies, demon lovers, the fairy host, and abduction into the Otherworld. Stories and motifs are followed down the centuries to reveal the changing nature of fairy lore, as it was told to famous figures like W.B. Yeats and Sir Walter Scott. All the research is based on primary sources and many errors about fairy tradition are laid to rest.

Jeremy Harte combines folklore scholarship with a lively style to show what the presence of fairies meant to people's lives. Like their human counterparts, the secret people could kill as well as heal. They knew marriage, seduction, rape and divorce; they adored some children and rejected others. If we are frightened of the fairies, it may be because their world offers an uncomfortable mirror of our own.

ISBN 1 872883 61 3. Demi 8vo (215 x 138 mm), 186 + vi pages, 6 line drawings, paperback £9.95

Also published by Heart of Albion Press

Explore Folklore

Bob Trubshaw

**'A howling success, which plugs a
big and obvious gap'**
Professor Ronald Hutton

There have been fascinating developments
in the study of folklore in the last twenty-
or-so years, but few books about British
folklore and folk customs reflect these exciting new approaches.
As a result there is a huge gap between scholarly approaches to
folklore studies and 'popular beliefs' about the character and
history of British folklore. *Explore Folklore* is the first book to
bridge that gap, and to show how much 'folklore' there is in
modern day Britain.

Explore Folklore shows there is much more to folklore than morris
dancing and fifty-something folksingers! The rituals of 'what we
do on our holidays', funerals, stag nights and 'lingerie parties' are
all full of 'unselfconscious' folk customs. Indeed, folklore is
something that is integral to all our lives – it is so intrinsic we do
not think of it as being 'folklore'.

The implicit ideas underlying folk lore and customs are also
explored. There might appear to be little in common between
people who touch wood for luck (a 'tradition' invented in the last
200 years) and legends about people who believe they have been
abducted and subjected to intimate body examinations by aliens.
Yet, in their varying ways, these and other 'folk beliefs' reflect the
wide spectrum of belief and disbelief in what is easily dismissed
as 'superstition'.

Explore Folklore provides a lively introduction to the study of
most genres of British folklore, presenting the more contentious
and profound ideas in a readily accessible manner.

ISBN 1 872883 60 5. Perfect bound, demi 8vo (215x138 mm),
200 pages, **£9.95**

Explore Mythology

Bob Trubshaw

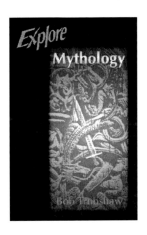

Myths are usually thought of as something to do with 'traditional cultures'. The study of such 'traditional' myths emphasises their importance in religion, national identity, hero-figures, understanding the origin of the universe, and predictions of an apocalyptic demise. The academic study of myths has done much to fit these ideas into the preconceived ideas of the relevant academics.

Only in recent years have such long-standing assumptions about myths begun to be questioned, opening up whole new ways of thinking about the way such myths define and structure how a society thinks about itself and the 'real world'.

These new approaches to the study of myth reveal that, to an astonishing extent, modern day thinking is every bit as 'mythological' as the world-views of, say, the Classical Greeks or obscure Polynesian tribes. Politics, religions, science, advertising and the mass media are all deeply implicated in the creation and use of myths.

Explore Mythology provides a lively introduction to the way myths have been studied, together with discussion of some of the most important 'mythic motifs' – such as heroes, national identity, and 'central places' – followed by a discussion of how these ideas permeate modern society. These sometimes contentious and profound ideas are presented in an easily readable style of writing.

ISBN 1 872883 62 1. Perfect bound. Demi 8vo (215 x 138 mm), 220 + xx pages, 17 line drawings. **£9.95**

Further details of all Heart of Albion titles online at
www.hoap.co.uk

All titles available direct from Heart of Albion Press.
Please add £1.30 p&p (UK only; email
albion@indigogroup.co.uk for overseas postage).

To order books or request our current catalogue please
contact

Heart of Albion Press

2 Cross Hill Close, Wymeswold

Loughborough, LE12 6UJ

Phone: 01509 880725

Fax: 01509 881715

email: albion@indigogroup.co.uk

Web site: www.hoap.co.uk